Macmillan McGraw-Hill

California Mathematics 2

Homework Practice and Problem-Solving Practice Workbook

Macmillan/McGraw-Hill

TO THE TEACHER These worksheets are the same ones found in the Chapter Resource Masters for *California Mathematics, Grade 2*. The answers to these worksheets are available at the end of each Chapter Resource Masters booklet.

Macmillan
McGraw-Hill

The McGraw·Hill Companies

Send all inquiries to:
Macmillan/McGraw-Hill
8787 Orion Place
Columbus, OH 43240

ISBN: 978-0-02-111966-0
MHID: 0-02-111966-X

Homework Practice/Problem Solving Practice Workbook, Grade 2

Printed in the United States of America.

1 2 3 4 5 6 7 8 9 10 079 17 16 15 14 13 12 11 10 09 08

CONTENTS

Name ____________________

1-1

Homework Practice

2NS1.2, 2MR1.2

Tens and Ones

Chapter Resources

Write how many tens and ones.

1. 23 = __2__ tens __3__ ones

__2__ tens + __3__ ones = __23__

tens	ones
2	3

2. 57 = ______ tens ______ ones

______ tens + ______ ones = ______

tens	ones

Use what you know about tens and ones to solve.

3. Mary puts her buttons in 2 groups of ten. She has 4 left over.

How many buttons does she have in all?

_____ tens + _____ ones =

_____ buttons

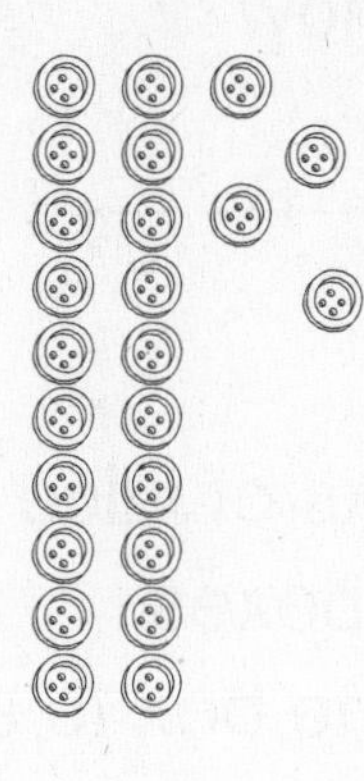

4. Ben has a sheet of 60 stamps. He cuts the sheet apart into groups of 10.

How many groups of 10 does he have?

_____ groups of 10

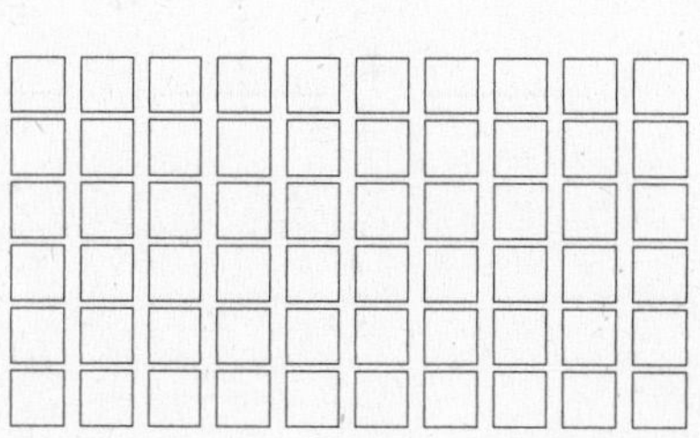

1-1

Name ____________________

Problem-Solving Practice

2NS1.2, 2MR1.2

Tens and Ones

Write an addition sentence to solve.

1. How many peas?

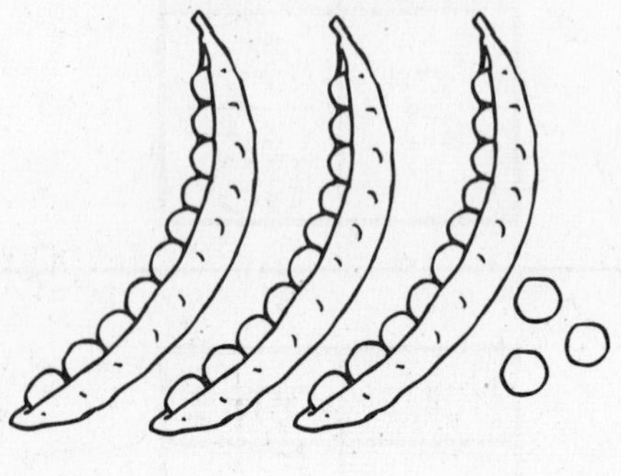

______ + ______ = ______

2. How many apples?

______ + ______ = ______

3. Vic uses cubes to show 7 tens and 5 ones. What number does he show?

______ + ______ = ______

4. Steve uses cubes to show 9 tens and 3 ones. What number does he show?

______ + ______ = ______

5. Mr. Hall has 3 packs of juice boxes. Each pack has 10 boxes. Draw a picture in the box to show how many boxes of juice Mr. Hall has. Then write your addition sentence.

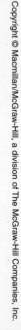

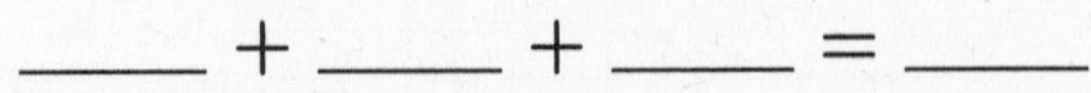

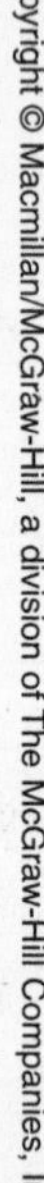

Name ____________________

1-2

Homework Practice

2NS1.1

Place Value to 100

Circle the value of the underlined digit.

1.	73 (7 underlined) 7 or 70	54 (4 underlined) 4 or 40	95 (5 underlined) 5 or 90
2.	13 (1 underlined) 1 or 10	37 (3 underlined) 3 or 30	83 (3 underlined) 3 or 30
3.	47 (7 underlined) 7 or 70	87 (7 underlined) 7 or 70	31 (3 underlined) 3 or 30
4.	17 (1 underlined) 1 or 10	25 (5 underlined) 5 or 50	94 (9 underlined) 9 or 90

Use place value to solve.

5. A bookcase has 43 books. There are 34 students in the class. Are there enough books for the students? How do you know?

____

____

____

____

____

6. There are 75 children in the concert. There are 8 boxes of song books. There are 10 books in each box. Is there a book for each child in the concert? How do you know?

____

____

____

____

____

Chapter Resources

1-2

Name ______________________________

Problem-Solving Practice

2NS1.1

Place Value to 100

Solve.

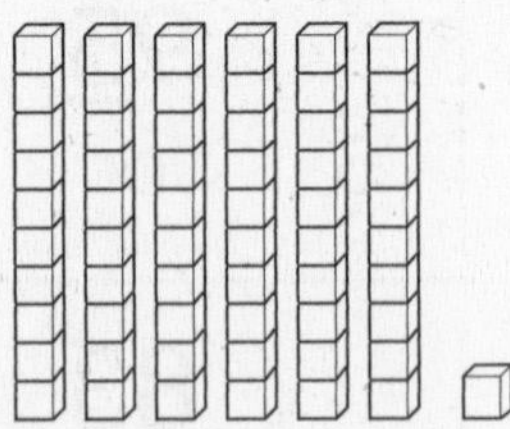

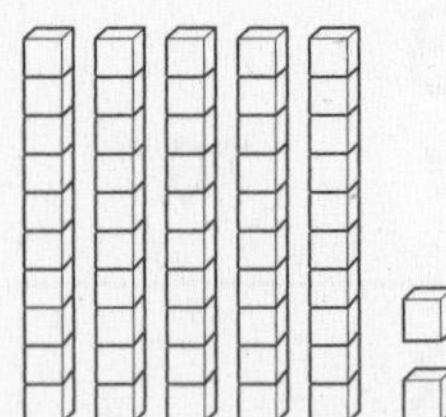

1. What is the value of the 6 in <u>6</u>1?

____

2. What is the value of the 2 in 5<u>2</u>?

____

3. Rita shows the number 12 with place-value models. She uses 2 ones. How many tens does she use?

____________ ten

4. Drew shows the number 76 with place-value models. He uses 7 tens. How many ones does he use?

____________ ones

5. Which two numbers use the digits 3 and 1?

__________ and __________

Which of these numbers has 3 tens?

____

6. Mr. Lo is thinking of a number. The ones digit is 8. The tens digit is 1. What is Mr. Lo's number?

____

Name ______________________

I-3

Homework Practice

2NS1.0, 2MR1.1

Problem-Solving Strategy: Logical Reasoning

Chapter Resources

Use logical reasoning to solve.

Show your work here.

1. Mike, Dara, and Leo are playing baseball. Mike bats first. Dara does not go third. Who bats third?

____

2. Ken, Joanne, Ted, and Minnie are waiting to see the school nurse. A boy will go first. Minnie will go second. Ted goes fourth. When does Joanne go?

____

3. Fran, Tom, and Barb have favorite colors. The colors are blue, red, and green. Fran likes green. Barb's favorite color starts with the same letter as her name. What is Tom's favorite color?

____

4. Kip, Sam, and Lisa each feed an animal at the park. The animals are a duck, a fish and a rabbit. Lisa's animal has fur. Sam's animal does not fly. Who feeds the duck?

____

1-4

Name ____________________

Homework Practice

2NS1.1, 2NS1.2

Read and Write Numbers

Chapter Resources

Write the number or the number words.

1.	seventy 70	59 fifty-nine	eighty-eight ______
2.	44 ______	twenty-two ______	nineteen ______
3.	90 ______	57 ______	seventy-three ______
4.	14 ______	15 ______	100 ______

Solve.

5. One of the biggest dinosaurs was 40 feet tall. Ann says it was forty feet tall. Is she right?

______

6. The same dinosaur was 85 feet long. Bill says it was eighty-eight feet long. Is he right?

______

7. One dinosaur had claws that were twelve inches long. Lupe says they were 14 inches long. Is she right?

______

8. One very small dinosaur was only about sixteen inches long. Sam says it was 16 inches long. Is he right?

______

Name ______________________________

1-4

Problem-Solving Practice

2NS1.1, 2NS1.2

Read and Write Numbers

Solve.

1. Tina says that 84 is the same as eighty-four. Is she right?

____

2. Steve has twenty-seven game cards. He gets thirty-two more from the store. He has fifty-nine now. Write the number sentence.

_______ + _______ = _______

3. Leon says that 25 + 11 = 36. Write the number words.

____________________ +

____________________ =

____

4. Pat says that 55 is the same as forty-five. Is he right?

____

5. Lars has 40 carrots. He gives nineteen to his friends. He has twenty-one left. Write the number sentence.

_______ − _______ = _______

6. Nan says that 96 − 4 = 92. Write the number words.

____________________ −

____________________ =

____

7. Help Jon write his family's ages in order of youngest to oldest: fourteen, sixty-seven, sixty-two, thirty-five, seven.

_______, _______, _______, _______, _______

Name ______________________________

I-5

Homework Practice

2NS6.0

Estimate Numbers

About how many? Circle your answer.

1.

about 10 about 30

2.

about 10 about 20

3.

about 10 about 20

4.

about 10 about 40

Estimate to solve.

5. Mrs. Todd buys 10 boxes of stars and 10 boxes of hats. Each box of stars has 10 stars. Most hat boxes have 10 hats. Some hat boxes have more than 10 hats. Is there a star for every hat? How do you know?

____

____

____

____

6. Ms. Benson is carrying 6 bags of apples. Most bags have 10 apples. Some bags have more than 10. Fifty-eight children are in line for apples. Is there an apple for each child? How do you know?

____

____

____

____

Name ______________________________

I-5

Problem-Solving Practice

2NS6.0

Estimate Numbers

Read and solve.

1. About how many balls does Jan have?

about ______ balls

2. About how many jacks does Jim have?

about ______ jacks

3. Brian wants to eat about 20 peanuts. Circle the bag he should choose.

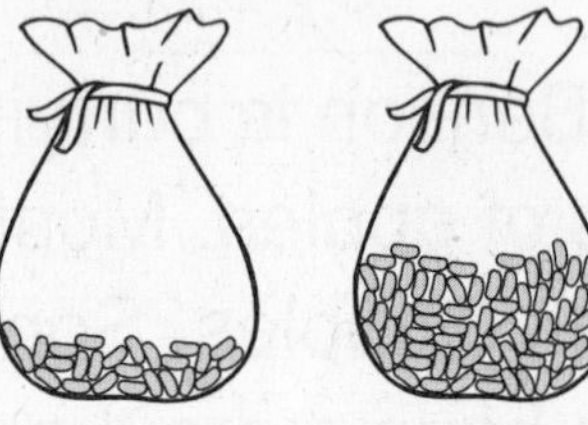

4. Leah needs about 50 chocolate chips to make muffins. Circle the bag she should choose.

5. Rob has an empty bag. About how many marbles will fill the empty bag?

about ______ marbles

10

6. Ken has an empty jar. About how many beans will fill the empty jar?

about ______ beans

20

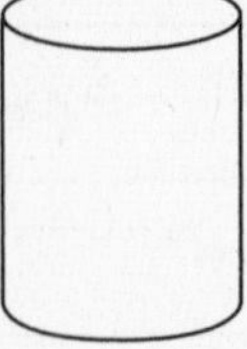

Name ______________________

1-6

Homework Practice

2NS1.3

Order Numbers

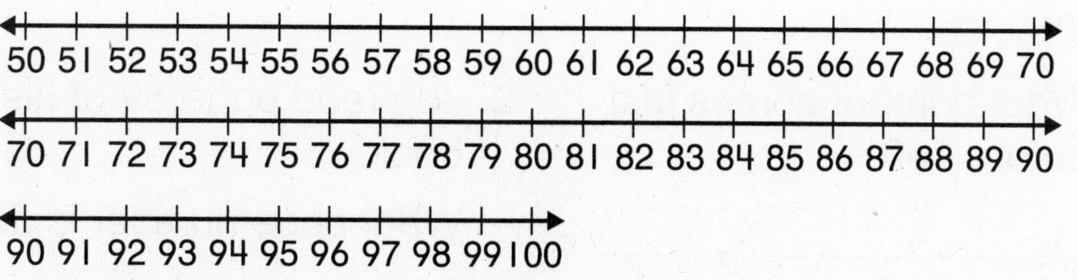

Use the number lines to fill in the blanks.

1. ______, 94, 95	73, 74, ______	57, 58, ______
2. ______, 69, 70	75, 76, ______	53, ______, 55
3. 93, ______, 95	61, 62, ______	______, 84, 85
4. 67, 68, ______	______, 51, 52	79, ______, 81
5. ______, 88, 89, ______	70, ______, ______, 73	

Use number order to solve.

6. On a test, Kay answers questions 1, 2, 3, 4, 5, 6 first. Next, she answers questions 8, 9, 10, 12, 14, 15.

What questions are left for her to answer?

____

7. Pat's favorite number has a 2 in the ones place. Think of the next number. What digit is in the ones place?

____

Name ______________________

1-6

Problem-Solving Practice

2NS1.3

Order Numbers

Solve.

1. What number comes just before 100?

____

2. Jon read page 69 of his book.

What page number is next?

____

3. Liz is the middle child of 3 kids. Her brother is 9. Her sister is 11. How old is Liz?

____

4. Mr. Morris gives his class clues about his age. His age is more than 30. It comes just before 40.

What is Mr. Morris's age?

____

5. Peng is making a map of his street. He wants to put the addresses in order from greatest to least. The addresses are 33, 31, 32, 34.

How can he order the numbers? Draw 4 houses to help solve.

6. Ms. Jones wants to put these number cards in order from least to greatest: 10, 5, 25, and 50.

How can she order the number cards? Draw the cards to help solve.

Name ______________________________

1-7

Homework Practice

2NS1.3

Compare Numbers

Chapter Resources

Compare. Write >, <, or =.

1. 94 (>) 49	53 ◯ 86	45 ◯ 25
2. 21 ◯ 22	47 ◯ 74	64 ◯ 46
3. 78 ◯ 78	56 ◯ 35	42 ◯ 89
4. 37 ◯ 39	39 ◯ 70	53 ◯ 38
5. 98 ◯ 89	13 ◯ 12	68 ◯ 76
6. 33 ◯ 31	48 ◯ 74	83 ◯ 83

Compare numbers to solve.

7. Look back over this page. Circle any number greater than 70.
Draw a box around numbers between 70 and 89.
Mark X on numbers with a 6 in the ones place.

What numbers have a circle, a square, and an "X"?

__________ __________

8. Cal and Ron are comparing homework.
Call says that 74 > 89.
Ron says that 89 > 74.

Who has the correct answer? How do you know?

____

____

____

Name ______________________

I-7

Problem-Solving Practice

2NS1.3

Compare Numbers

Solve. Write >, <, or = to show the answer.

1. Anna's favorite number is 75.
   Jack's favorite number is 60.

   Which number is greater?

   ____

2. Pete's favorite number is 99.
   Lana's favorite number is 100.

   Which number is less?

   ____

3. On Saturday, 92 people go to the zoo.
   On Sunday, 95 people go to the zoo.

   Are there more people at the zoo on Saturday or Sunday?
   How do you know?

   ____

4. On Friday, the baseball game lasts 79 minutes.
   On Saturday, the baseball game lasts 74 minutes.

   Is the game shorter on Friday or Saturday?
   How do you know?

   ____

5. Eighteen inches of snow fall in December.
   Twenty-two inches of snow fall in January.

   Which month has more snow, December or January?
   How do you know?

   ____

Name ____________________

1-8 Homework Practice

2SDAP2.1, 2SDAP2.2

Patterns

Draw a picture to continue the pattern.

1\. A A A B A A A B

____

2\.   

_______ _______ _______

____

3\.   

A B B A B B A B B

____

4\. A B C A B C

____

Find the pattern and solve.

5\. On Monday, Sal has drum class. On Tuesdays, he has a piano lesson. On Wednesday and Thursday he has singing lessons. Use the letters A, B, and C to write a letter pattern that can has the same pattern as Sal's music lessons.

____

6\. Betty is making a bracelet with colored beads. She is using this pattern: green, green, blue, gold. How can Betty use letters to show her pattern?

____

Name ______________________________

I-8

Problem-Solving Practice

2SDAP2.1, 2SDAP2.2

Patterns

Use patterns to solve.

1. Nan is painting this pattern on her bedroom floor: two circles, two squares, two circles, two squares. How can Nan use the letters A and B to describe her pattern?

   ____

2. Lily is painting a wall in her room. She wants to use a triangle followed by two circles, followed by one square. Use the letters A, B, and C to describe the pattern she will use.

   ____

3. The third grade class has started to paint a long wall in school. They have painted the pattern shown here. Draw the next two parts of the pattern in the box.

   ○, ○, △, ○, ○, △

4. Kyle is drawing patterns on paper. His pattern is ABBCABBC. The A means a triangle. The B means a square. The C means a circle. Draw the pattern twice in the box.

Name ____________________

1-9

Homework Practice

2MR1.1, 2NS2.2

Problem-Solving Investigation: Choose a Strategy

Chapter Resources

Problem-Solving Strategies
Draw a Picture
Logical Reasoning
Act it Out

Solve.

Show your work here.

1. Shane, CJ, and Vera wash, dry, and put away the dishes. Shane does not dry the dishes. Vera puts away the dishes. CJ gives Vera the dry dishes. Who washes the dishes?

____

2. Sara is setting the table. She sets a fork, napkin, plate, fork, napkin, plate, and a fork. What should she set next?

____________________.

3. Nina makes four pies. BJ buys a cake. Grandma Jenkins makes 3 giant cookies. How many desserts does the family have in all?

____

1-10

Name ______________________________

Homework Practice

2SDAP2.1, 2SDAP2.2

Patterns on a Hundred Chart

Use the hundred chart to skip count.

1	2	3	4	5	6	7	8	9	10
11	12	13	14	15	16	17	18	19	20
21	22	23	24	25	26	27	28	29	30
31	32	33	34	35	36	37	38	39	40
41	42	43	44	45	46	47	48	49	50
51	52	53	54	55	56	57	58	59	60
61	62	63	64	65	66	67	68	69	70
71	72	73	74	75	76	77	78	79	80
81	82	83	84	85	86	87	88	89	90
91	92	93	94	95	96	97	98	99	100

1. Skip count by 4s.

   36, 40, 44, 48, ______, ______, ______, ______

2. Skip count by 6s.

   36, 42, 48, ______, ______, ______

3. Skip count by 12s.

   12, 24, 36, ______, ______, ______

Use a number pattern to solve.

4. Raul wants to use a pattern to skip count backward by tens. He starts at 95. What can you tell Raul about the ones digits in his skip count?

   The ones digit will be ______.

5. James color skip counts by 6s. He starts at 6 and stops at 50. Tammy color skip counts the 12s on the same chart. She starts at 12 and stops at 50. What numbers will be colored by both children?

   ____

Name ______________________________

1-10

Problem-Solving Practice

2SDAP2.1, 2SDAP2.2

Patterns on a Hundred Chart

Use a number pattern to solve.

1	2	3	4	5	6	7	8	9	10
11	12	13	14	15	16	17	18	19	20
21	22	23	24	25	26	27	28	29	30
31	32	33	34	35	36	37	38	39	40
41	42	43	44	45	46	47	48	49	50
51	52	53	54	55	56	57	58	59	60
61	62	63	64	65	66	67	68	69	70
71	72	73	74	75	76	77	78	79	80
81	82	83	84	85	86	87	88	89	90
91	92	93	94	95	96	97	98	99	100

1. Ryan skip counts by 5 four times. John skip counts by 4 five times. Both boys start at 0. They both stop when they reach the same number. What is the number?

   ______

2. Mia color skip counts by 6 eight times. Sara color skip counts by 8 six times. They both start at 0. What numbers do Mia and Sara both color?

   ____

3. Xavier is making a spinner for a game. He starts counting at 30. He skip counts by 10. What numbers will he write on the spinner?

   ____

4. Enzo is making a game spinner for a game. He starts counting at 15. He skip counts by 15. What numbers will he write on the spinner?

   ____

Name ______

2-1

Homework Practice

2AF1.1, 2MR3.0

Addition Properties

Find each sum.

1. $\begin{array}{r} 7 \\ +2 \\ \hline \end{array}$ $\begin{array}{r} 2 \\ +7 \\ \hline \end{array}$

2. $\begin{array}{r} 3 \\ +9 \\ \hline \end{array}$ $\begin{array}{r} 9 \\ +3 \\ \hline \end{array}$

3. $\begin{array}{r} 4 \\ +9 \\ \hline \end{array}$ $\begin{array}{r} 9 \\ +4 \\ \hline \end{array}$

4. $\begin{array}{r} 7 \\ +1 \\ \hline \end{array}$ $\begin{array}{r} 1 \\ +7 \\ \hline \end{array}$

5. 7 + 5 = ______

5 + 7 = ______

6. 6 + 2 = ______

2 + 6 = ______

7. 1 + 7 = ______

7 + 1 = ______

8. 5 + 4 = ______

4 + 5 = ______

Solve.

9. The zoo has 4 striped snakes. It has 2 yellow snakes, too.

How many total snakes?

______ snakes

10. There are 2 brown bears. There are 4 black bears.

How many bears are there?

______ bears

11. There are 7 blue birds. There are 3 red birds. How many birds are there in all?

______ birds

2-1

Name ____________________

Problem-Solving Practice

2AF1.1, 2NS2.2

Addition Properties

Use what you know about addition properties to solve.

1. What two addition facts can April use to find the total number of dots on this domino?

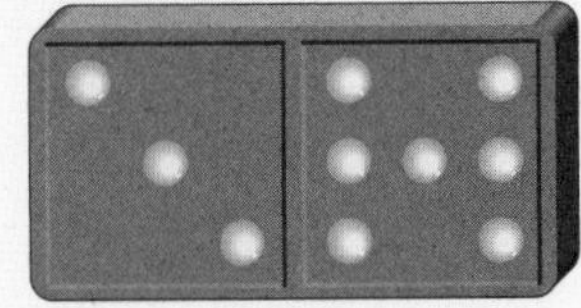

_____ + _____ = _____   _____ + _____ = _____

2. What two addition facts can Ken write to match these base-ten blocks?

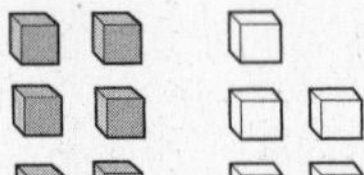

_____ + _____ = _____

_____ + _____ = _____

3. Manuel's team scores 8 runs in the first game. They score |||| runs in the second game. Show two ways you can find the total number of runs.

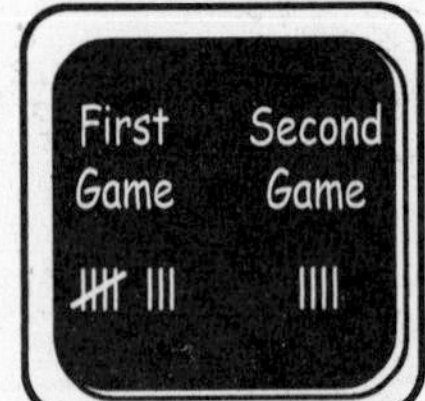

_____ ◯ _____ ◯ _____   _____ ◯ _____ ◯ _____

4. Cassie knows that 7 + 0 = 7. How can she use the same addends to write the fact another way?

_____ + _____ = _____

5. Emma knows that 4 + 5 = 9. How can Emma use the same addends to write the fact another way?

_____ + _____ = _____

Name ______________________________

2-2

Homework Practice

2NS2.2

Count On to Add

Chapter Resources

Use the numbers square.
Count on to add.

1	2	3	4	5
6	7	8	9	10
11	12	13	14	15
16	17	18	19	20
21	22	23	24	25

$\begin{array}{r} 4 \\ +1 \\ \hline \end{array}$ $\quad$ $\begin{array}{r} 2 \\ +6 \\ \hline \end{array}$ $\quad$ $\begin{array}{r} 1 \\ +8 \\ \hline \end{array}$

1. $\begin{array}{r} 2 \\ +4 \\ \hline \end{array}$ $\quad$ $\begin{array}{r} 2 \\ +8 \\ \hline \end{array}$ $\quad$ $\begin{array}{r} 3 \\ +9 \\ \hline \end{array}$ $\quad$ $\begin{array}{r} 4 \\ +3 \\ \hline \end{array}$ $\quad$ $\begin{array}{r} 6 \\ +2 \\ \hline \end{array}$

2. $\begin{array}{r} 1 \\ +4 \\ \hline \end{array}$ $\quad$ $\begin{array}{r} 3 \\ +1 \\ \hline \end{array}$ $\quad$ $\begin{array}{r} 4 \\ +6 \\ \hline \end{array}$ $\quad$ $\begin{array}{r} 8 \\ +3 \\ \hline \end{array}$ $\quad$ $\begin{array}{r} 6 \\ +1 \\ \hline \end{array}$

3. $\begin{array}{r} 3 \\ +3 \\ \hline \end{array}$ $\quad$ $\begin{array}{r} 1 \\ +6 \\ \hline \end{array}$ $\quad$ $\begin{array}{r} 4 \\ +2 \\ \hline \end{array}$ $\quad$ $\begin{array}{r} 8 \\ +1 \\ \hline \end{array}$ $\quad$ $\begin{array}{r} 6 \\ +3 \\ \hline \end{array}$

4. 8 + 3 = ______ $\quad$ 9 + 3 = ______ $\quad$ 7 + 1 = ______

5. 5 + 2 = ______ $\quad$ 6 + 2 = ______ $\quad$ 2 + 5 = ______

Count on to solve.

6. Ken had 4 fish.
Now Ken has 7 fish.
How many fish did he buy?

______ fish

7. Cherie has some trading cards. She gets 3 more cards. Now she has 9.
How many cards did she have at the start?

______ cards

Name ____________________

2-2

Problem-Solving Practice

2NS2.2

Count On to Add

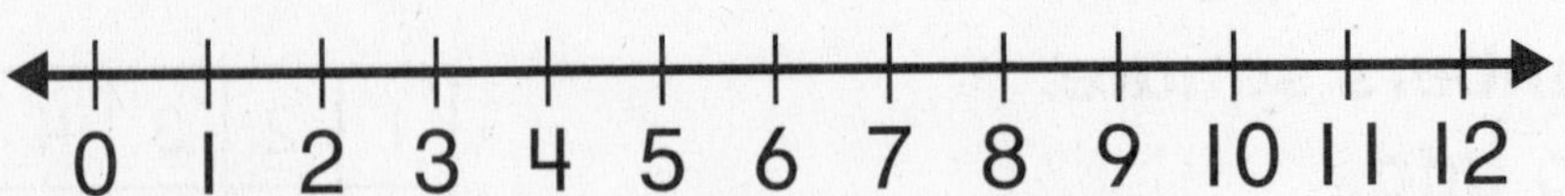

Count on to add.

1. Linda and Nell put their eggs in a basket. There are 6 eggs in all. Nell put in 4 eggs. How many eggs did Linda put in?

   _____ eggs

2. The Brown farm has 2 pigs. There are 5 pigs at the Green farm. How many more pigs do the Greens have?

   _____ pigs

3. Sal's cow gives 3 pails of milk in the morning. She gives 5 pails in the afternoon. How much milk does Sal's cow give in one day?

   _____ pails

4. A farm grows 4 kinds of green cabbage, 3 kinds of tomatoes, and 2 kinds of red cabbage. How many kinds of cabbage do they grow?

   _____ kinds of cabbage

5. Quackers Farm keeps five ducks in the front pond. They keep two ducks in the back pond. How many ducks are at the farm?

   _____ ducks

6. Peter grows seven kinds of red peppers. His brother grows two kinds of green peppers. How many kinds of peppers do they grow in all?

   _____ kinds of peppers

7. Mr. Rey's fish farm has five tanks. He has four tanks of baby fish. He also has adult fish. How many tanks of adult fish does he have?

   _____ tanks of adult fish

8. Gus sells 6 bunches of corn. His sister sells 2 bunches of corn. How many bunches of corn did they sell altogether?

   _____ bunches

2-3

Name ____________________

Homework Practice

2MR2.2

Problem-Solving Strategy: Act It Out

Chapter Resources

Preparation: Connecting cubes are needed for this activity.

Solve. Use connecting cubes or tally marks to act it out.

1. There is a number between 26 and 29. It has a 7 in the ones place. What is it?

   ____

2. Randy puts his toy cars in a row. The red car is behind the black car. The black car is behind the yellow car. Which color car is in front?

   ____

3. May has 4 apples and 19 grapes. How many more grapes does she have?

   ____

4. Tom sees 4 ducks. 1 flies away. How many ducks are left?

   ____

5. Betty walked 15 miles. Josh walked 12 miles. How many more miles did Betty walk than Josh?

   ____

6. Ella has 3 dolls: a white doll, a blue doll, and a red doll. The white doll is not the tallest. The blue doll is the shortest. Which doll is the tallest?

   ____

Name ______________________________

2-4

Homework Practice

2NS2.2

Doubles

Chapter Resources

Add.

1.

7	6	9	8	8
+ 4	+ 6	+ 3	+ 5	+ 4

2.

3	9	7	8	6
+ 7	+ 9	+ 5	+ 8	+ 4

3. 5 + 6 = ______ 9 + 0 = ______ 7 + 3 = ______

4. 7 + 7 = ______ 2 + 6 = ______ 3 + 9 = ______

Draw a picture to solve.
Write the number sentence.

5. Kim has 9 pairs of socks.Ron buys the same number of socks.

How many pairs of socks do they have?

____ + ____ = ____ socks

6. There are 7 pairs of twins in the fourth grade this year.

How many fourth grade students are twins?

____ + ____ = ____ twins

7. Circle all of the doubles facts on this page.

Name ______________________________

2-4

Problem-Solving Practice

2NS2.2

Doubles

Write the number sentence. Use doubles to solve.

1. Terry cut 8 snowflakes from white paper. Derek cut 8 snowflakes from blue paper.

many paper snowflakes did they make?

_____ + _____ = _____

2. Mr. Bean sells 5 melons to Ed. He sells the same number of melons to Jose.

How many melons did Mr. Bean sell in all?

_____ + _____ = _____

3. Carmen has six new trading cards. Miguel has an equal number of cards.

What is the total number of cards they have?

_____ + _____ = _____

4. Lisa finds 9 markers in her room. She finds an equal number in the kitchen.

What is the sum of all the markers Lisa found?

_____ + _____ = _____

5. Mel works at a shoe store. Monday he sold 10 pairs of shoes. 1 pair equals 2 shoes. How many shoes did Mel sell?

_____ ◯ _____ ◯ _____

6. Paula rides the bus to school for 7 blocks. She also rides the bus home. How many blocks does she ride in 1 day?

_____ ◯ _____ ◯ _____

7. Claudia is making a rug. It can hold 4 pairs of boots. How many boots will fit on the rug?

_____ ◯ _____ ◯ _____

8. Dan used 3 stamps. His mom used 3 more. How many stamps did they use in all?

_____ ◯ _____ ◯ _____

Name ______________________________

2-5

Homework Practice

2NS2.1

Near Doubles

Find the sum.

1. $\begin{array}{r} 7 \\ +\ 6 \\ \hline \end{array}$ $\begin{array}{r} 8 \\ +\ 9 \\ \hline \end{array}$ $\begin{array}{r} 6 \\ +\ 6 \\ \hline \end{array}$ $\begin{array}{r} 6 \\ +\ 5 \\ \hline \end{array}$

2. $\begin{array}{r} 7 \\ +\ 7 \\ \hline \end{array}$ $\begin{array}{r} 5 \\ +\ 4 \\ \hline \end{array}$ $\begin{array}{r} 7 \\ +\ 8 \\ \hline \end{array}$ $\begin{array}{r} 9 \\ +\ 8 \\ \hline \end{array}$

3. 5 + 7 = ______ 9 + 6 = ______ 4 + 3 = ______

4. 9 + 9 = ______ 5 + 6 = ______ 8 + 10 = ______

Use what you know about near doubles to solve.

5. Look at all the sums above. Circle the **sums** of doubles.

6. Look at the addends above. Draw a box around the addends that are near doubles.

7. Vik gets 8 dollars for pulling weeds. Anya mows the grass and gets a dollar more than Vik. Write an addition sentence that tells how many dollars Vik and Anya get in an hour.

______ + ______ = ______

8. Marlene washes 7 pairs of jeans on Tuesday. She washes one less pair on Thursday. Write a near double addition sentence to tell the total number of jeans Marlene washes.

_____ + _____ = _____ jeans

Name ______________________________

2-5

Problem-Solving Practice

2NS2.1

Near Doubles

Use what you know about near doubles to solve.

1. Paula knows she can use two different doubles facts to find the sum of 8 + 9. What are they?

   ______ + ______ = ______

   ______ + ______ = ______

2. Scotty is looking for two different doubles facts that he can use to find the sum of 7 + 6. What are they?

   ______ + ______ = ______

   ______ + ______ = ______

3. Chris buys 9 boxes of juice for the baseball team. Allen buys one less box than Chris. Write an addition fact to find the total number of boxes Chris and Allen buy.

   ______ + ______ = ______

4. One store gives 6 baseball mitts to the team. Another store gives one more mitt than the first. Write an addition fact that tells the total number of mitts.

   ______ + ______ = ______

5. Mr. Gomez buys four new bats for the team. Mr. Moore buys one more bat than Mr. Gomez. What is the total number of bats they give?

   ______ + ______ = ______

6. On Wednesday, the Reed family buys 7 tickets to the game. On Thursday, they buy one more ticket than they did on Wednesday. How many tickets does the Reed family have?

   ______ + ______ = ______

7. This year the Tigers made 1 more goal than they made last year. Last year they made eight goals. How many goals did they make in both years?

   ______ + ______ = ______

Name ______________________________

2-6

Homework Practice

2NS2.2

Make a 10

Chapter Resources

Add. Remember to make a 10 first.

1.
$$\begin{array}{r} 7 \\ +4 \\ \hline \end{array} \quad \begin{array}{r} 4 \\ +8 \\ \hline \end{array} \quad \begin{array}{r} 9 \\ +7 \\ \hline \end{array} \quad \begin{array}{r} 7 \\ +6 \\ \hline \end{array} \quad \begin{array}{r} 2 \\ +9 \\ \hline \end{array}$$

2.
$$\begin{array}{r} 3 \\ +9 \\ \hline \end{array} \quad \begin{array}{r} 7 \\ +5 \\ \hline \end{array} \quad \begin{array}{r} 8 \\ +8 \\ \hline \end{array} \quad \begin{array}{r} 9 \\ +4 \\ \hline \end{array} \quad \begin{array}{r} 8 \\ +7 \\ \hline \end{array}$$

3. $7 + 7 =$ ______ $4 + 8 =$ ______ $9 + 5 =$ ______

4. $8 + 9 =$ ______ $9 + 7 =$ ______ $6 + 9 =$ ______

5. Look at the addends in the questions above. Circle any addends that you can add using near doubles.

Solve. Remember to first make a 10.

6. Raul wins 8 chess matches on Saturday. He wins 5 matches on Sunday. Complete the two addition sentences to show how many games he won all weekend.

   8 + ______ ______
   10 + ______ ______

7. Carla's team won 6 games last year. This year, her team has won 9 games. Complete the two addition sentences to show how many games her team won both years.

   ______ + 9 ______
   ______ + 10 ______

8. Show how you would explain "Make a 10" to someone who had never heard of it.

Name ____________________

2-6 Problem-Solving Practice

2NS2.2

Make a 10

Solve.

1. Mel bakes 6 loaves of bread for the bake sale. His sister bakes 8 loaves.

How many loaves of bread will they bring to the bake sale?

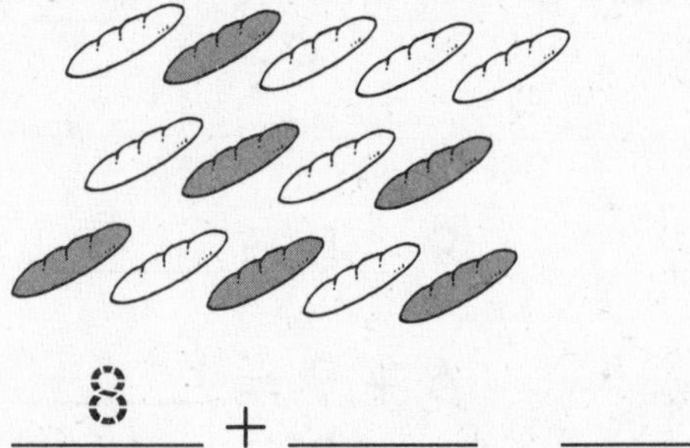

__8__ + ______ ______

2. Pauline's mom makes 7 pies for the bake sale. Ann's mom makes 9 pies.

How many pies will they bring to the bake sale?

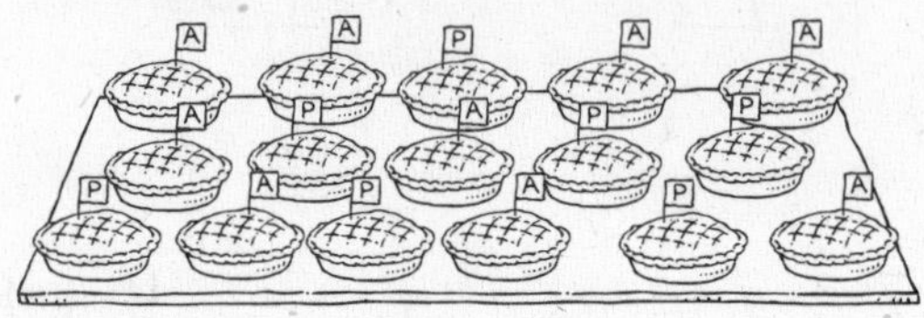

______ + __9__ ______

3. Ms. Ling uses part of the money from the bake sale to buy art supplies. She buys 5 boxes of red markers and 8 boxes of blue markers.

How many boxes of markers did she buy in all?

______ boxes of markers

4. Mrs. Quinn buys some pencils. Mr. Lopez buys seven boxes of pencils. Together they bought 15 boxes.

How many boxes of pencils did Mrs. Quinn buy?

______ boxes of pencils

5. David 's class sent 9 letters to the president. Ann's class also sent letters. The two classes sent 17 letters in all.

How many letters did Ann's class send?

______ letters

6. Mrs. Han's class has five fish in their fish tank. Ms. Johnson's class has nine fish in their tank.

How many more fish does Ms. Johnson's class have?

______ fish

Name ______________________

2-7

Homework Practice

2AF1.1

Add Three Numbers

Find each sum.

1.

6	6	3	7	6
5	2	3	4	4
+ 4	+ 8	+ 9	+ 3	+ 5
15				

2.

1	3	7	8	6
9	3	6	4	4
+ 4	+ 0	+ 6	+ 2	+ 0

3.

7	6	4	9	6
3	1	2	8	6
+ 5	+ 6	+ 6	+ 1	+ 6

4.

7	6	8	7	7
3	1	4	8	6
+ 3	+ 6	+ 2	+ 2	+ 3

Solve.

5. Benji has 6 fish. TJ has 7 fish and 3 dogs.
Max has 4 fish.

How many fish are there?

______ fish

6. The doctor's office has fish tanks. Five of the fish are guppies. Six fish are angel fish. Eight fish are mollies. How many fish in all?

______ fish

Name ______________________________

2-7

Problem-Solving Practice

2AF1.1

Add Three Numbers

Complete the number sentence. Find each sum.

1. The zoo has 5 black bears, 5 brown bears, and 2 polar bears. How many bears are at the zoo?

   ______ + ______ + ______ = ______ bears

2. In the baby zoo, 2 cubs are playing, 3 cubs are sleeping, and 3 cubs are eating. How many cubs are at the baby zoo?

   ______ + ______ + ______ = ______ cubs

3. Ellie feeds 3 lambs and 4 goats. Tom feeds 7 ducks. How many animals did they feed in all.

   ______ + ______ + ______ = ______ animals

4. Six seals are on the high rocks. Four seals and three seagulls are on the low rocks. Five seals are in the water. How many seals are there in all?

   ______ + ______ + ______ = ______ seals

5. Eric draws one lion, six birds, one tree, two houses, and six deer. How many animals does he draw altogether?

   ______ + ______ + ______ = ______ animals

6. There are 9 boys, 3 teachers, 2 dogs, and 7 girls watching the water show. How many people are watching the show in all?

   ______ + ______ + ______ = ______ people

Name ______________________________

2-8

Homework Practice

2MR1.1, 2AF1.1

Problem-Solving Investigation: Choose a Strategy

Choose a strategy and solve.

Problem-Solving Strategies
Draw a picture
Use logical reasoning
Act it out

1. Tracy read 4 books about lions. Greg read 2 books on tigers. Buster read 6 books on bears.

   How many books did the three friends read in all?

   ______ books

2. Last month Larry got three math games. This month he got eight spelling games. Next month he plans to get two reading games.

   How many games will Larry have at the end of next month?

   ______ games

3. Shea watched 5 videos on dinosaurs. Drew watched 4 videos on space travel. Manuel watched 6 videos on racing.

   How many videos did the children watch in all?

   ______ videos

4. After school, Ms. Blaine put 8 books on the top shelf. She put 2 books on the middle shelf and 8 books on the bottom shelf.

   How many books did Ms. Blaine put on the shelves?

   ______ books

5. The new library has 4 big, soft chairs. It has 7 wood chairs and 3 rocking chairs.

   How many chairs does the library have in all?

   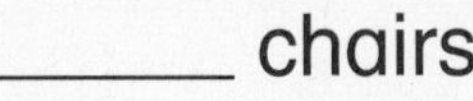 chairs

Name ______________________________

3-1

Homework Practice

2NS2.2

Count Back to Subtract

Count back to subtract. Use the number line.

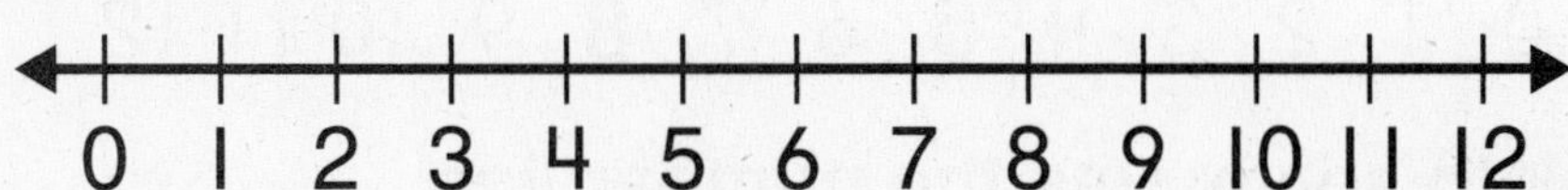

1. 6 − 2 = ______ Start at ______. Count back ______.

2. 12 − 4 = ______ Start at ______. Count back ______.

3. 11 − 2 = ______ Start at ______. Count back ______.

4. 7 − 2 = ______ Start at ______. Count back ______.

5. 9 − 3 = ______ Start at ______. Count back ______.

6. 12 − 3 = ______ Start at ______. Count back ______.

7. 10 − 1 = ______ Start at ______. Count back ______.

Count back to solve.

8. A paper clip holder has twelve clips. Alex uses five paper clips.

How many paper clips are left?

______ paper clips

9. Marty buys 11 pencils. She uses 3 pencils.

How many pencils does Marty have left?

______ pencils

Name ______________________________

3-1

Problem-Solving Practice

2NS2.2

Count Back to Subtract

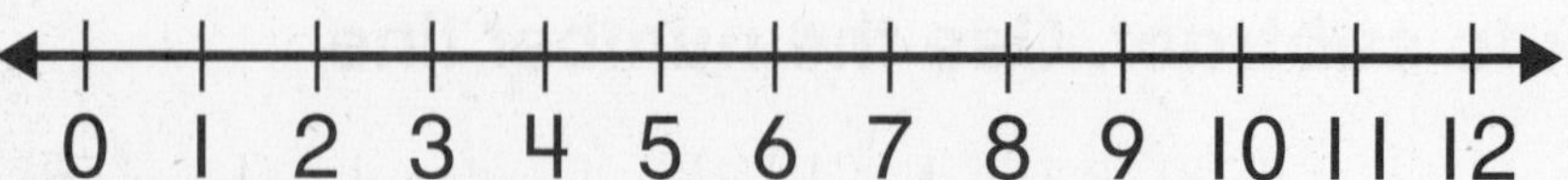

Count back to solve. Use the number line.

1. Tanya has 12 blocks. She gives 5 away.
   How can you count back to find out how many she has now?
   Start at _____. Count back _____ to _____.
   _____ blocks

2. Ricky has 10 oranges. He uses 6 to make juice.
   How can you count back to find out how many are left?
   Start at _____. Count back _____ to _____.
   _____ oranges left

3. Madison's class needs to plant 10 trees. They plant 3 trees. Write a number sentence to tell how many trees are left to plant.
   _____ – _____ = _____
   _____ trees

4. Hank needs to wash 9 windows. He washes 6 windows. Write a number sentence to tell how many windows are left to wash.
   _____ – _____ = _____
   _____ windows

5. Twelve cars and four trucks come to the car wash.
   How many more cars than trucks are at the car wash?
   _____ cars

Name ______________________________

3-2

Homework Practice

2NS2.2, 2MR1.2

Subtract All and Subtract Zero

Chapter Resources

Subtract.

1. 12 − 3 = ____   11 − 3 = ____   6 − 6 = ____   9 − 0 = ____

2. 6 − 0 = ____   9 − 9 = ____   7 − 3 = ____   4 − 0 = ____

3. 3 − 3 = ____   4 − 4 = ____   5 − 5 = ____   10 − 2 = ____

4. 8 − 0 = ______   10 − 3 = ______   7 − 0 = ______

5. 11 − 2 = ______   5 − 3 = ______   7 − 7 = ______

Count back to solve.

6. There are 8 candles on a cake. Javier blows out all 8 candles.

How many candles are still burning?

______ candles

7. Eleven children come to the party. Three leave early.

How many children are still at the party?

______ children

Name ______________________________

3-2

Problem-Solving Practice

2NS2.2, 2MR1.2

Subtract All and Subtract Zero

Write a number sentence for each. Then solve.

1. 3 bees buzz near a flower. None fly away.

   How many bees are near the flower?

   ______ – ______ = ______

   ______ bees

2. 5 sparrows are in the nest. They all fly away.

   How many sparrows are still in the nest?

   ______ – ______ = ______

   ______ sparrows

3. 8 ducks are swimming in a pond. They all fly away.

   How many ducks are in the pond?

   ______ ◯ ______ ◯ ______

   ______ ducks

4. Mrs. Keen feeds 8 squirrels. None run away.

   How many squirrels are left?

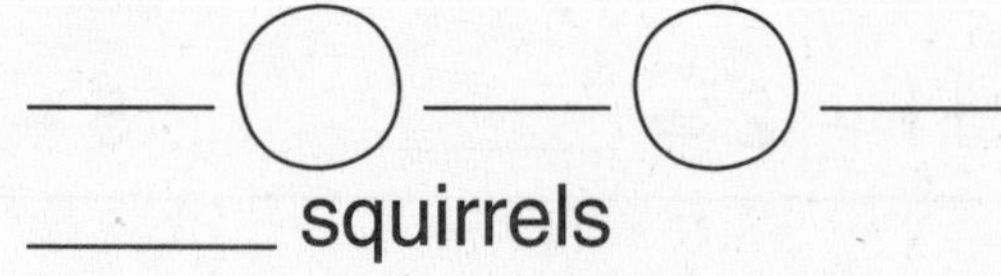

   ______ squirrels

5. Miguel catches seven spiders. He lets them all go.

   How many spiders are left?

   ______ spiders

6. Write a story that this number sentence would solve.

   5 – 5 = 0.

   ____

Name ____________________

3-3

Homework Practice

2NS2.2, 2MR1.2

Use Doubles to Subtract

Subtract.

1.

5	10	4	8	12
– 3	– 2	– 0	– 4	– 6

2.

10	4	18	16	14
– 1	– 1	– 9	– 8	– 7

3. 9 – 3 = ______ 8 – 3 = ______ 7 – 1 = ______

4. 10 – 5 = ______ 10 – 3 = ______ 9 – 9 = ______

Solve. Write the number sentence.

5. Brian has 18 CDs. He gives 9 CDs to his brother. How many CDs does Brian still have?

______ – ______ = ______

6. Anita checks out 14 library books. She reads seven of the books. How many books does she still have to read?

______ – ______ = ______

7. Look back over this page. Circle the problems where you used doubles to subtract.
Draw a box around any difference less than 3.

Name ____________________

3-3

Problem-Solving Practice

2NS2.2, 2MR1.2

Use Doubles to Subtract

Write the number sentence. Use doubles.

1. Fran and her grandmother pick 16 pumpkins. They use 8 pumpkins for pie.

How many pumpkins are left?

_____ – _____ = _____

_____ pumpkins

2. Luis picks 14 tomatoes. His dad uses 7 tomatoes for salsa.

How many tomatoes does Luis have left?

_____ – _____ = _____

_____ tomatoes

3. Neal has 10 baskets of apples. He gives 5 baskets to his neighbor.

How many baskets of apples does Neal keep?

_____ – _____ = _____

_____ baskets

4. The Horn family plants 6 rows of corn. They pick 3 rows of corn.

How many rows of corn are left to pick?

_____ – _____ = _____

_____ rows of corn

5. Delia bakes eighteen cherry pies. She sells some pies at a farmer's market.

She has nine pies left. How many pies did she sell?

_____ ◯ _____ ◯ _____

_____ cherry pies

6. Doug brings 12 peppers to market. At the end of the day, he has six peppers.

How many peppers did he sell?

_____ ◯ _____ ◯ _____

_____ peppers

3-4

Name ______________________________

Homework Practice

2SDAP2.1, 2MR1.0

Problem-Solving Strategy: Find a Pattern

Chapter Resources

1. Kim plants tulips. She plants 3 tulips in row one. She plants 6 tulips in row two. She plants 9 tulips in row 3. If she keeps the same pattern, how many tulips will she plant in row 6?

Row	1	2	3			
Tulips	3	6	9			

There will be _____ tulips in row 6.

2. Terry and Pat play a game with colored squares. The pictures show the game after 1, 2, and 3 turns. If the pattern continues, how many squares will be in the game after 8 turns?

1 Turn

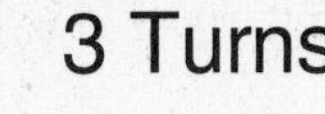

2 Turns

3 Turns

Turn	1	2	3					
Squares	2	4	6					

There will be ____ squares in the game after 8 turns.

3. Beth's Bookstore starts with 20 puzzle books. An hour later, they have 17 puzzle books. After 2 hours there are 14 books.

If the pattern stays the same, when will there be only 2 puzzle books left to sell?

Puzzle Books	20	17	14	11			
Hours	Open	1	2	3			

There will be only 2 puzzle books after _____hours.

Name ______________________

3-5

Homework Practice

2NS2.1, 2MR3.0

Relate Addition to Subtraction

Chapter Resources

Use addition facts to subtract.

1. $\begin{array}{r} 7 \\ +5 \\ \hline \end{array}$ $\begin{array}{r} 12 \\ -5 \\ \hline \end{array}$ | $\begin{array}{r} 6 \\ +9 \\ \hline \end{array}$ $\begin{array}{r} 15 \\ -9 \\ \hline \end{array}$ | $\begin{array}{r} 8 \\ +5 \\ \hline \end{array}$ $\begin{array}{r} 13 \\ -5 \\ \hline \end{array}$

2. $\begin{array}{r} 4 \\ +7 \\ \hline \end{array}$ $\begin{array}{r} 11 \\ -7 \\ \hline \end{array}$ | $\begin{array}{r} 7 \\ +3 \\ \hline \end{array}$ $\begin{array}{r} 10 \\ -3 \\ \hline \end{array}$ | $\begin{array}{r} 4 \\ +0 \\ \hline \end{array}$ $\begin{array}{r} 4 \\ -0 \\ \hline \end{array}$

3. $\begin{array}{r} 9 \\ +3 \\ \hline \end{array}$ $\begin{array}{r} 12 \\ -3 \\ \hline \end{array}$ | $\begin{array}{r} 6 \\ +6 \\ \hline \end{array}$ $\begin{array}{r} 12 \\ -6 \\ \hline \end{array}$ | $\begin{array}{r} 7 \\ +8 \\ \hline \end{array}$ $\begin{array}{r} 15 \\ -8 \\ \hline \end{array}$

4. 9 + 8 = ______ | 8 + 5 = ______ | 7 + 7 = ______

17 − 8 = ______ | 13 − 5 = ______ | 14 − 7 = ______

Write a number sentence to solve.

5. Dean has 15 books. He reads 8 of them. How many books does Dean have left to read?

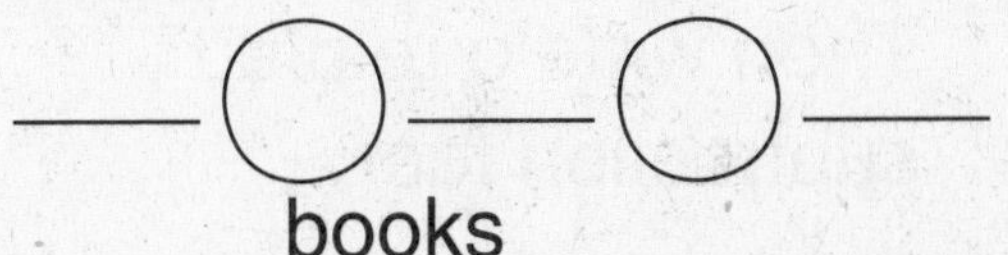

______ books

6. Fay paints 8 pictures in March. She paints 9 pictures in April. How many pictures does Fay paint?

____ ◯ ____ ◯ ____

______ pictures

Name ______________________________

3-5

Problem-Solving Practice

2NS2.1, 2MR3.0

Relate Addition to Subtraction

Write a number sentence to solve.
Then write a related fact.

1. 5 children start soccer on Monday. 4 more children start soccer on Wednesday.

How many children in all play soccer?

_____ + _____ = _____

_____ children

_____ − _____ = _____

2. The tennis team has 16 players. 8 players leave the team.

How many players are still on the team?

_____ − _____ = _____

_____ players

_____ + _____ = _____

3. Ten boys join the model train club. Two boys move away.

How many boys are in the club?

_____ ◯ _____ ◯ _____

_____ boys

_____ ◯ _____ ◯ _____

4. Six players start a game club. Nine new players join.

How many players are in the game club now?

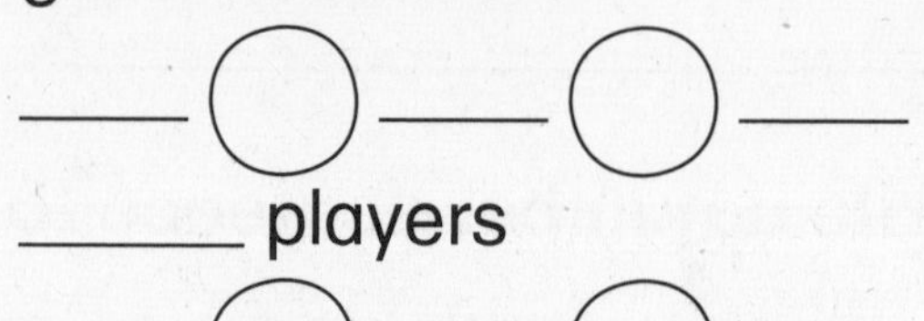

_____ players

_____ ◯ _____ ◯ _____

5. Write an addition story. Use the numbers 4, 6, and 10.

____

6. Write the number sentence for your story.
Then write a related subtraction fact.

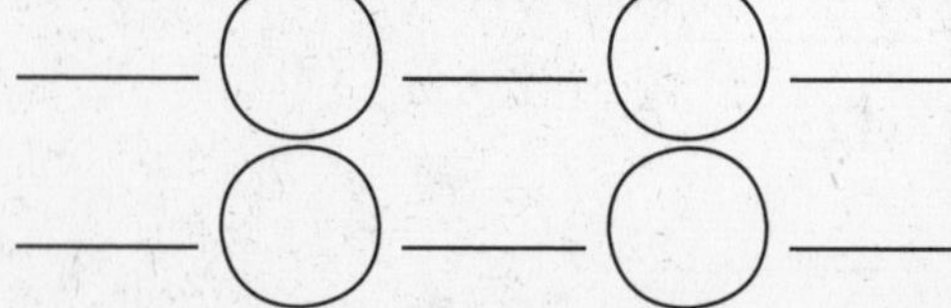

3-6

Name ____________________

Homework Practice

2NS2.1

Missing Addend

Chapter Resources

Find each missing addend.

1.	7	12	□	15	8
	+ 8	− □	+ 6	− 6	+ □
	□	8	15	□	13
2.	4	17	7	16	8
	+ □	− □	+ 9	− □	+ 6
	11	8	□	7	□
3.	9	12	□	□	7
	+ □	− 5	+ 6	+ 6	+ □
	12	□	14	12	13

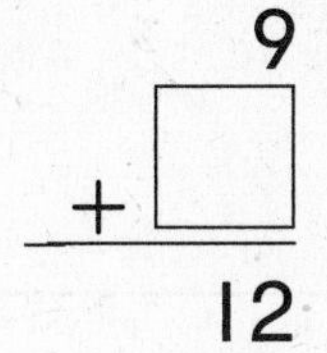

4. 9 + □ = 17 $\quad$ 8 + 3 = □ $\quad$ □ + 7 = 13

Solve. Use related facts.

5. David and his friends are flying 16 kites. Some kites get trapped in trees. 7 kites are still flying.

How many kites are in the trees?

7 + □ = 16

16 − 7 = □

______ kites

6. The scouts have 15 boats. They put some boats in the pond. 9 boats are left on land.

How many boats did the scouts put into the pond?

9 + □ = 15

15 − 9 = □

______ boats

Name ___

3-6

Problem-Solving Practice

2NS2.1

Missing Addends

Solve. Use related facts.

1. Anna buys 7 plants. She wants 12 plants.

   How many more plants does Anna need?

   7 + ☐ = 12

   12 − 7 = ☐

   Anna needs ___ more plants.

2. J.J. needs 14 flower boxes. He has 6 flower boxes.

   How many more flower boxes does J.J. need?

   6 + ☐ = 14

   14 − 6 = ☐

   J.J. needs ___ more flower boxes.

3. Garden City plans to put 14 trees in a park. The city has 9 trees.

   How many more trees does the city need?

   9 + ☐ = 14

   14 − 9 = ☐

   The city needs ☐ more trees.

4. Louis has 7 roses. He wants 15 roses.

   How many more roses does Louis need?

   7 + ☐ = 15

   15 − 7 = ☐

   Louis needs ☐ more roses.

Name ______________________________

3-7

Homework Practice

2NS2.1, 2MR3.0

Fact Families

Chapter Resources

Complete each fact family.

1.

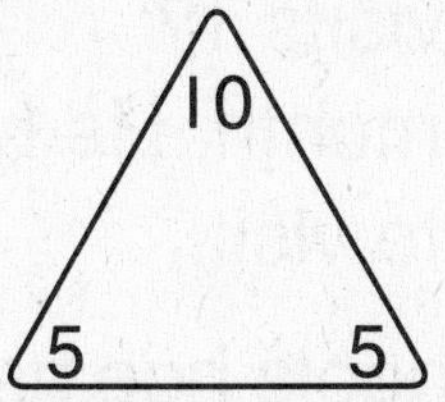

5 + ____ = 10

10 − ____ = 5

2.

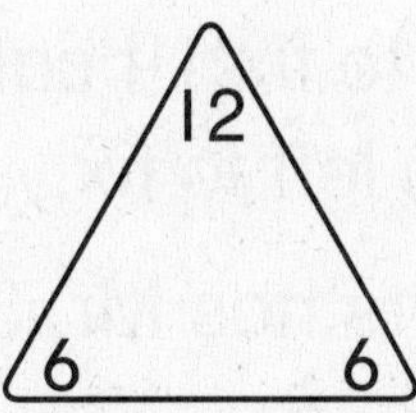

6 + ____ = 12

12 − ____ = 6

3.

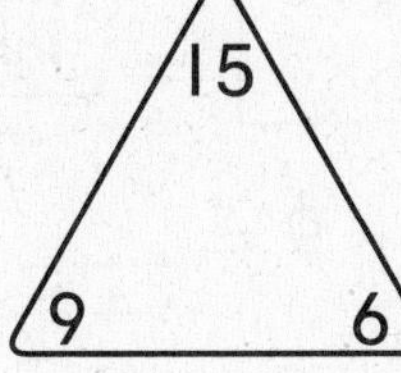

6 + 9 = ____

9 + 6 = ____

15 − 9 = ____

15 − 6 = ____

4.

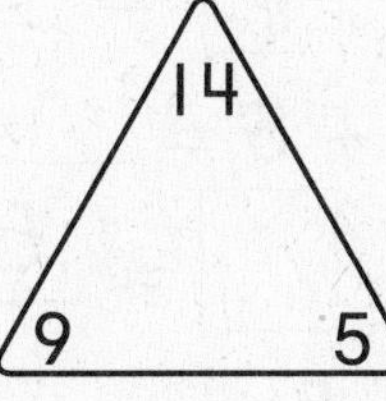

5 + 9 = ____

9 + 5 = ____

14 − 9 = ____

14 − 5 = ____

5.

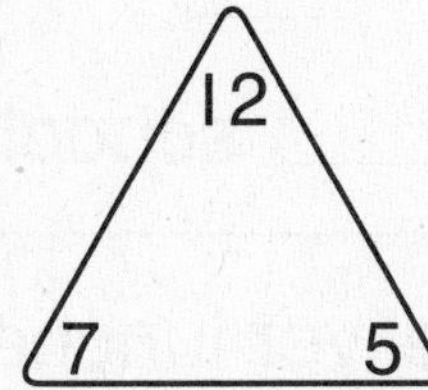

7 + ____ = 12

____ + 7 = 12

12 − ____ = 7

12 − ____ = 5

6.

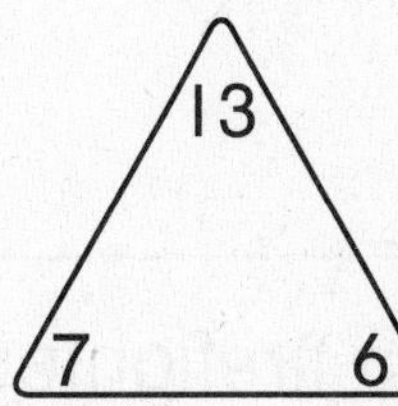

____ + 7 = 13

7 + ____ = 13

13 − ____ = 6

13 − ____ = 7

Solve. Write the fact family.

7. Lori made 7 bracelets. Then, she made 9 more.

How many total bracelets did Lori make?

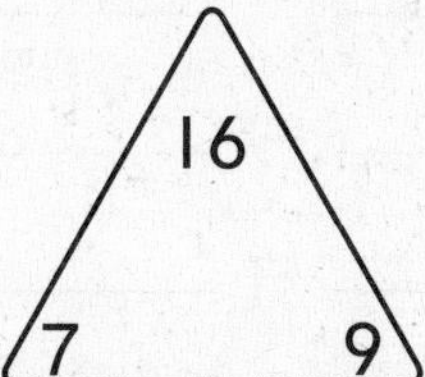

____ + ____ = ____ ____ − ____ = ____

____ + ____ = ____ ____ − ____ = ____

Lori made ______ bracelets in all.

Name ______________________________

3-7

Problem-Solving Practice

2NS2.1, 2MR3.0

Fact Families

Solve. Write the number sentences in the fact family.

1. Mr. Sims has to fix 14 cars. He has 5 cars left to fix.

   How many cars has Mr. Sims already fixed?

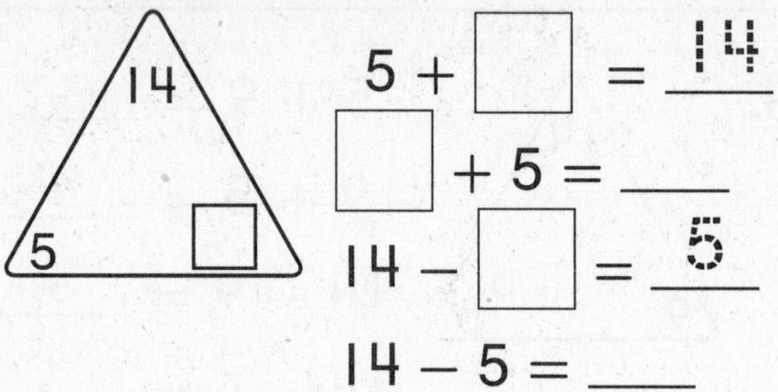

   ___ cars

2. Officer Smith visits 17 schools each month. He has 9 schools left to visit.

   How many schools has he already visited?

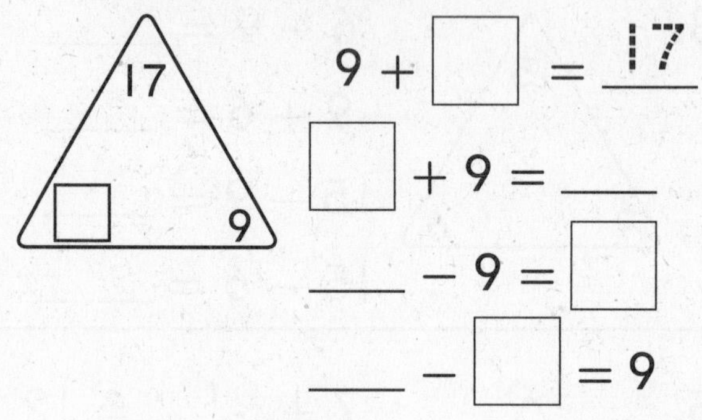

   He has visited ___ schools.

3. Ms. Grimes is a firefighter. She plans 15 fire drills each month. She has 8 drills left to plan.

   How many fire drills has she already planned?

   ______ + ______ = ______

   ______ + ______ = ______

   ______ − ______ = ______

   ______ − ______ = ______

   She has planned ______ fire drills.

4. Doug & Son deliver lunches to 16 schools a day. Today, they have 9 schools left to go to.

   How many deliveries did they make?

   ______ + ______ = ______

   ______ + ______ = ______

   ______ − ______ = ______

   ______ − ______ = ______

   They have made ______ deliveries.

Name ____________________

3-8

Homework Practice

2AF1.2, 2MR1.1

Problem-Solving Investigation: Choose a Strategy

Problem-Solving Strategies
Find a Pattern
Logical Reasoning
Write a Number Sentence

Solve.

Show your work here.

1. Ray is painting red, yellow, and blue stripes. He paints a yellow stripe next to the blue stripe. The red stripe is not first. He paints a red stripe next to the blue stripe. What is the order of the stripes?

   ________, ________, ________

2. Mrs. Ash buys 16 rolls of wallpaper. Nine rolls are for the downstairs. The rest are for the bedrooms. How many rolls of wallpaper are for the bedrooms?

   ______ rolls

3. Sue buys 17 cans of paint. Four cans are blue. Three cans are green. Two cans are red. The rest of the cans are white. How many cans of paint are white?

   ______ cans of white

4-1

Name ______________________________

Homework Practice

2SDAP1.1, 2SDAP1.4

Take a Survey

Ask your classmates what breakfast foods they like best. Complete the chart. Use tally marks to show data.

Favorite Breakfast Foods	
Cereal	
Eggs	
Fruit	
Toast	

Use the survey to answer each question.

1. Which food did your classmates like least?

____

2. Which got more votes, cereal or toast?

____

3. How many like eggs and fruit best?
Write a number sentence to solve.

_____ + _____ = _____

4. Tina wants to make breakfast for your entire class. How many people will she need to make cereal for?

____

4-1

Name ____________________

Problem-Solving Practice

2SDAP1.1, 2SDAP1.4

Take a Survey

Solve.

1. Lin wants to take a survey about favorite games. Which question should she ask? Put a ✓ beside the answer.

__ Where do you like to play?

__ What is your favorite game?

__ Who are your friends?

2. Jim is taking a survey about favorite games. He asks 7 students. How many tally marks will his chart show?

______ tally marks

Favorite Amusement Ride	Tally	Total
Roller Coaster	𝍸 I	6
Ferris Wheel	𝍸 𝍸	10
Bumper Cars	IIII	4

3. Which ride got the most votes?

____

Which ride got the least votes?

____

4. How many more people voted for the Ferris wheel than the bumper cars?

______ more people

Name ______________________________

4-2

Homework Practice

2SDAP1.2, 2SDAP1.4

Picture Graphs and Pictographs

Preparation: Crayons are needed for this activity.

The students voted for their favorite color. Show the votes on the picture graph. Use the data. Draw one crayon for each vote. Use the graph to answer each question.

Data:	Red	Blue	Green	Purple
	𝍸 I	𝍸	III	IIII

Our Favorite Color

Red	
Blue	
Green	
Purple	

1. How many more students chose red than green? ______

2. How many students voted for either green or purple? ______

3. How many students voted in all? ______

4. If two more students vote for green, which color will now have the least votes? ____________. Add their votes to the graph.

5. Now look at the graph. Color the rows that show the same number of votes. ____________________

Name ______________________

4-2

Problem-Solving Practice

2SDAP1.2, 2SDAP1.4

Picture Graphs and Pictographs

Use the graph to solve the problems.

Favorite Flower	
tulip	❀ ❀ ❀ ❀ ❀
daisy	❀ ❀
rose	❀ ❀ ❀
lily	❀

Each ❀ stands for 2 votes

1. Which flower got the most votes? ________

2. How many votes did the lily get?

   ______ votes

3. Which flower got 6 votes?

   ____

4. How many total votes did the daisy and the rose get?

   ______ votes

5. How many more votes did the tulip get than the daisy? Write a number sentence to find out. ________________

   The tulip got ______ more votes than the daisy.

6. **Use the data from the pictograph above to make a picture graph.**

Favorite Flower	
tulip	
daisy	
rose	
lily	

Name ____

4-3

Homework Practice

2MR2.2, 2AF1.3

Problem-Solving Strategy: Write a Number Sentence

Use the graph to answer the questions. Write a number sentence to solve.

Mr. Bunn's Class Lunch	
Peanut Butter & Jelly Sandwich	卌 卌 ||
Salad	||||
Tuna Sandwich	卌 |

1. How many more students ate peanut butter and jelly sandwiches than salads? ______ − ______ = ______

2. How many students ate either a salad or a tuna sandwich?

   ______ + ______ = ______

3. How many students ate a sandwich?

   ______ + ______ = ______

4. Drew wants to know how many more tuna sandwiches than salads. ______ − ______ = ______

5. Mr. Bunn wants to bring 6 extra salads for the next class lunch. How many salads then?

   ______ + ______ = ______

Name ______________________________

4-4

Homework Practice

2SDAP1.1, 2SDAP1.4

Bar Graphs

Chapter Resources

Preparation: Crayons are needed for this activity.

Ms. Costa's class took a survey. Look at their tally chart.

Our Favorite Music	
Country	卌 ||
Rock	卌 ||||
Jazz	||||

Make a bar graph with the data. Then, answer the questions.

Our Favorite Music

			10
			9
			8
			7
			6
			5
			4
			3
			2
			1
Country	Rock	Jazz	

1. How many students voted for jazz or country? Write a number sentence to solve. ______ + ______ = ______

2. How many more students voted for rock than country? Write a number sentence to solve. ______ − ______ = ______

3. How many students voted? ______

4. Trey, Chris, and Ruth voted. Trey's favorite music got 4 votes. Chris' favorite music did not get the most votes. What is Ruth's favorite music? ________

Name ______________________________

4-4

Problem-Solving Practice

2SDAP1.1, 2SDAP1.4

Bar Graphs

Use the bar graph to solve each problem.

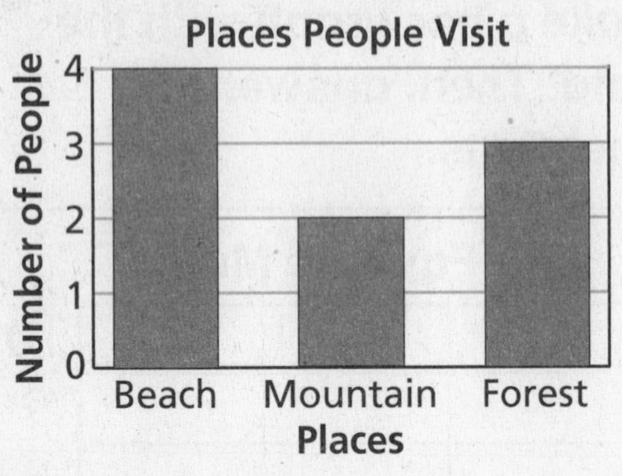

1. How many people visited the beach?

   ______ people

2. How many people visited the forest?

   ______ people

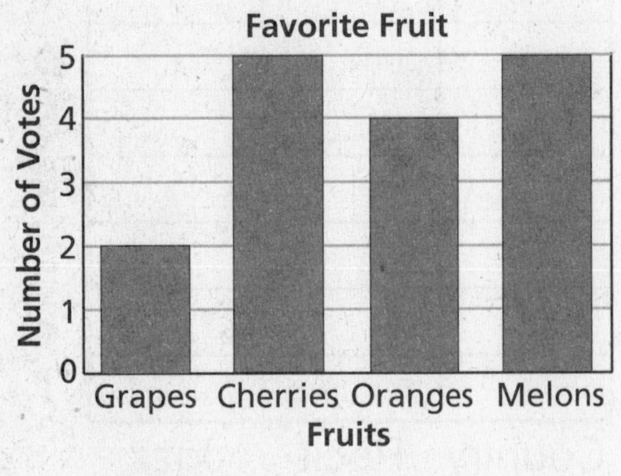

3. Which fruit or fruits got the most votes?

   ____

4. Which got the fewest votes?

   ____

   How many votes did this fruit get?

   ______ votes

5. How many more votes did oranges get than grapes?

   Write a number sentence to compare.

   ____

   ______ more votes

6. How many people voted for their favorite fruit in all? Write the number sentence to find out.

   ____

   ______ people voted in all.

Name ______________________________

4-5

Homework Practice

2SDAP1.2, 2AF1.3

Different Ways to Show Data

Preparation: Crayons are needed for this activity.

Use the data. Make a tally chart, a pictograph, and a bar graph to show the data.

Our Favorite Instruments	
Piano	
Guitar	
Drums	

Our Favorite Instruments	
Piano	
Guitar	
Drums	

Key: Each ♪ = 2 instruments.

Our Favorite Instruments

Piano										
Guitar										
Drums										
	1	2	3	4	5	6	7	8	9	10

Name ____________________

4-5 Problem-Solving Practice

2SDAP1.2, 2AF1.3

Different Ways to Show Data

Complete the graphs. Use the graphs to solve.

Favorite Snacks	
Pretzels	
Popcorn	
Fruit	

Each stands for 2 votes

1. How many children voted for popcorn?

______ children

2. How many votes did pretzels get?

______ votes

3. How many more children voted for pretzels than popcorn? Write a number sentence.

______ – ______ = ______

______ children

Favorite Snacks		
Snack	Tally	Total
Pretzels	卌		
Popcorn	||	
Fruit	||||	

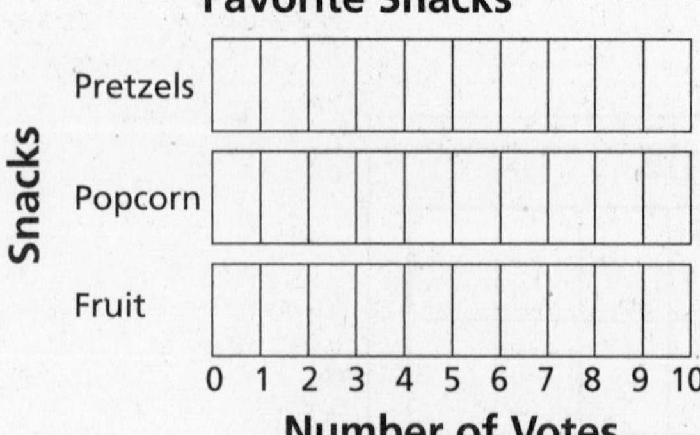

4. Which snack got the greatest number of votes?

____

Which graph did you use to answer? Explain.

____

4-6

Name ______

Homework Practice

2SDAP1.3, 2SDAP1.4

Range and Mode

Mrs. Sand's class recorded how many trees they have in their yards at home. Find the mode. Find the range.

Mrs. Sand's Class Trees				
Number of Trees	4	5	6	7
Number of yards	|||	~~||||~~ |	|||	|

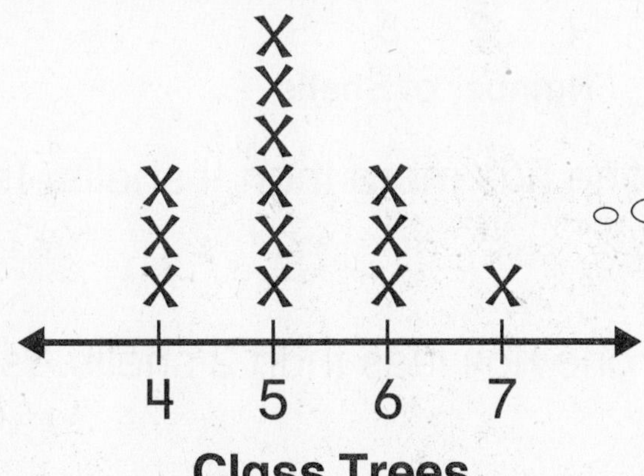

Class Trees

Remember: **mode** is the most; **range** is the difference.

Use the graph to solve.

1. What is the greatest number of trees? ______

2. What is the least number of trees? ______

3. What is the range? ______

4. What is the mode? ______

5. Nick's yard has 5 trees. His mom wants to plant 2 new trees. Would this change the mode? ______

6. Elena's yard has 4 trees. Her father has to cut down 1 tree. What is the range now? ______

4-6

Name ______________________________

Problem-Solving Practice 2SDAP1.3, 2SDAP1.4

Range and Mode

Use the graph to solve.

Number of Seashells We Have

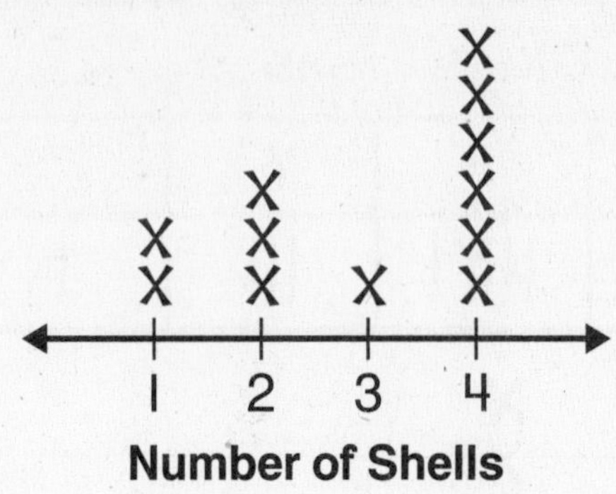

1. Lee says that no one has more than 4 shells. Is she right?

______

2. Nick says that no one has less than 2 shells. Is he right?

______

3. Leo wants to keep his shells in a box. What is the greatest number of shells he would have to plan for? ______

4. Sara has 4 shells. Her mom did not have any shells. Sara gave 1 shell to her. Does this change the range? ______

5. Rhonda, Tom, Liz, and Miguel all have 4 shells. If they each find 1 more shell, does the mode change? ______
If so, what is the new mode? ______

6. Would Rhonda, Tom, Liz, and Miguel's new shells change the range? Write a number sentence to solve.

______ − ______ = ______

____

Name ______

Homework Practice

2MR1.1, 2AF1.2

Problem-Solving Investigation: Choose a Strategy

Solve.

Problem-Solving Strategies
Draw a Picture
Find a Pattern
Make a Table

1. Look at the table. Do you see a pattern? ______ If so, use the pattern to complete the table. How long does it take to get to New Mountain Station? ______

Town	Travel Time from Mayfield Station
Greenville Station	2 hours
Oaktown Station	4 hours
New Mountain Station	6 hours
Windy Hollow Station	hours

2. Olive, Sean, and Luis are saving soup labels. Olive has 10, Sean has 7, and Luis has 13. How many more soup labels does Luis have than Sean? ______

3. Mr. Bell wants his students to put on their gloves before going outside. There are 21 students in Mr. Bell's class. Each student has 2 gloves. How many gloves do Mr. Bell's students have in all? ______

4. Suzie, Simon, and Sen each had 4 bottles of sports drink during their softball game. How many bottles of sports drink did they have in all? ______

5-1

Name ______________________

Homework Practice

2NS2.3

Add Tens

Add.

1. 7 tens + 2 tens = _____ tens

70 + 20 = _____

6 tens + 2 tens = _____ tens

60 + 20 = _____

2. 1 ten + 7 tens = _____ tens

10 + 70 = _____

5 tens + 4 tens = _____ tens

50 + 40 = _____

3. $20 + 40$ $\quad$ $30 + 40$ $\quad$ $40 + 30$ $\quad$ $20 + 60$ $\quad$ $50 + 30$

4. $30 + 30$ $\quad$ $40 + 20$ $\quad$ $80 + 10$ $\quad$ $10 + 60$ $\quad$ $20 + 70$

Add tens to solve.

5. One box holds 10 paper clips. Another box holds 50 paper clips. How many paper clips in all?

_____ paper clips

6. Lydia collects 20 red pencils. She has twice as many black pencils as red pencils. How many pencils does Lydia have in all?

_____ pencils

Name ______________________

5-1

Problem-Solving Practice

2NS2.3

Add Tens

Solve. Use addition facts to help.

1. Jake has 50 blue marbles. His sister has 40 green marbles. How many marbles do they have in all?

   ______ marbles

2. Sue has 10 guppies. Her friend Halley has 20. How many guppies do the girls have in all?

   ______ guppies

3. Corey has 60 animal stamps. He has 20 space stamps. How many stamps does he have altogether?

   ______ stamps

4. Ella takes 30 pictures of her trip. Her brother, Ed, takes 40 pictures. How many total pictures do they have?

   ______ pictures

5. Minny has 30 plain stickers. She has twice as many striped stickers. How many stickers does she have in all?

   ______ stickers

6. Steve has thirty paper airplanes. His friend Sal has ten fewer airplanes. How many paper airplanes do the two friends have?

   ______ planes

Name ____________

5-2 Homework Practice

2AF1.2

Count On Tens and Ones

Count on to add. Write the sum.

1. 47 + 40 = ____ 73 + 20 = ____ 42 + 50 = ____ 24 + 24 = ____

2. 22 + 33 = ____ 41 + 56 = ____ 34 + 22 = ____ 34 + 35 = ____

3. 28 + 40 = ____ 38 + 1 = ____ 77 + 11 = ____

4. 65 + 30 = ____ 76 + 2 = ____ 55 + 44 = ____

Count on to solve.

5. There are thirty-three children in swim class. There are forty children in diving class. How many children are there in all?

   ____ children

6. Twenty-seven boys and thirty-two girls are learning volleyball. How many children in all are learning volleyball?

   ____ children

7. Look back over the page. Circle any sum that is the result of adding doubles.

   Then draw two circles around any sum that is the result of adding doubles plus one.

Name ________________________________

5-2

Problem-Solving Practice

2AF1.2

Count On Tens and Ones

Count on to solve.

1. There are 15 banana muffins and 13 carrot muffins at a bake sale. Write a number sentence that tells how many muffins there are.

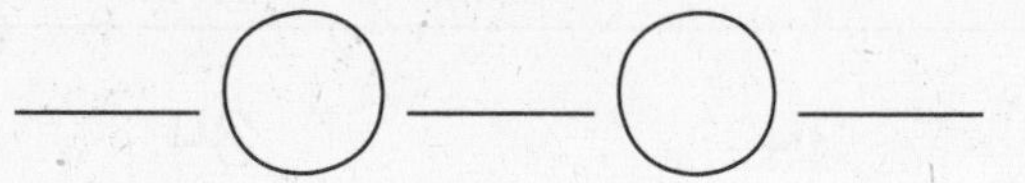

2. Mr. Chan sells 32 cartons of milk on Monday. He sells 27 cartons of milk today. Write a number sentence that tells how many total cartons of milk he sells.

____ ◯ ____ ◯ ____

3. Glenda sells 46 puppy treats. Rene sells 33 cat treats. How many treats did they sell in all?

_____ treats

4. Mrs. Hall cuts 30 pieces of cake. Mr. Cobb cuts 48 pieces of cake. How many pieces of cake are there in all?

_____ pieces of cake

5. Toni buys tart for 30 cents. Lou buys a pie for twice that amount. Write a number sentence to tell how much Lou pays for his pie.

____ ◯ ____ ◯ ____

Write a number sentence to tell how much Toni and Lou spend together.

____ ◯ ____ ◯ ____

6. Hal spends 35 cents on milk and 20 cents for one fruit bar. Tia buys two fruit bars. Write a number sentence that tells how much Tia spends on fruit bars.

____ ◯ ____ ◯ ____

How much do Hal and Tia spend in all?

____ cents

Name ______________________________

5-3

Homework Practice

2AF1.2, 2MR1.0

Problem-Solving Strategy: Work Backward

Chapter Resources

Solve. Work backward. Show your work.

1. Uncle Joe plans to bring 12 more hotdogs to the picnic than Aunt Patty. Aunt Patty will bring 5 more hotdogs than Grandpa. Grandpa will bring 10 hotdogs. How many hotdogs will Uncle Joe bring?

   ______ hotdogs

   ____

2. Selma brings 5 more chickens than her sister Lee does. Lee brings 4 chickens. Ira brings 6 more chickens than Selma. How many chickens does Ira bring?

   ______ chickens

   ____

3. Aunt Alice bakes seven pies for the picnic. Emil bakes four more pies than Aunt Alice. Sue bakes six more pies than Emil. How many pies does Sue bake for the picnic?

   ______ pies

   ____

4. Carol always brings melons to the picnic. This year, she will bring 5 more melons than Kayla. Kayla will bring 3 more melons than Matt. Matt will bring 2 melons. How many melons will Carol bring to the picnic?

   ______ melons

   ____

Name ______________________________

5-4

Homework Practice

2AF1.0, 2MR1.2

Regroup Ones as Tens

Chapter Resources

Use WorkMat 6 and [tens rod] to add.

		Add the ones. Add the tens.	Do you regroup?	Write the sum.
1.	24 + 7	____ tens ____ ones	yes no	24 + 7 = ____
2.	36 + 8	____ tens ____ ones	yes no	36 + 8 = ____
3.	28 + 5	____ tens ____ ones	yes no	28 + 5 = ____
4.	47 + 4	____ tens ____ ones	yes no	47 + 4 = ____
5.	23 + 3	____ tens ____ ones	yes no	23 + 3 = ____

6. Last year, 12 bands marched in the parade. This year, 9 bands marched in the parade. How many bands marched in all?

_____ bands

7. Nine clowns walk in Saturday's parade. Twenty-three clowns drive a tiny car. How many clowns are in Saturday's parade?

_____ clowns

8. Look over the problems in this page. Draw a circle around any sum that has a 3 in the ones place.
Then draw a box around any sum that has a 5 in the tens place.

Name ______________________________

5-4

Problem-Solving Practice

2AF1.0, 2MR1.2

Regroup Ones as Tens

Add. Tell how many ones and tens.

1. Rich planted 18 seeds last year. This year he plants 8 more. How many seeds has he planted in all?

______ ten ______ ones

______ seeds

2. Hal has 63 shells. He adds 3 more to his collection. How many shells does he have now?

______ tens ______ ones

______ shells

3. Casey has 35 nuts. Grandmother gives him 7 more. How many total nuts does Casey have?

______ tens ______ ones

______ nuts

4. Mrs. Steven made 65 yarn bunnies. This week she will make 6 more bunnies. How many bunnies will she have then?

______ tens ______ ones

______ bunnies

5. Kat has eighteen books. Her sister has nine books. Together, how many books do the sisters have?

______ ten ______ ones

______ books

6. Marvin wins thirty-five marbles this summer. He won six marbles last year. How many did he win in both years?

______ tens ______ ones

______ marbles

Name ______________________________

5-5

Homework Practice

2AF1.0, 2MR1.2

Add One-Digit Numbers and Two-Digit Numbers

Use WorkMat 6 and [ten-rod] to add.

1.

[1]	[ ]	[1]	[1]
5 6	8 4	6 6	2 9
+ 8	+ 3	+ 6	+ 4
___	___	___	___

2.

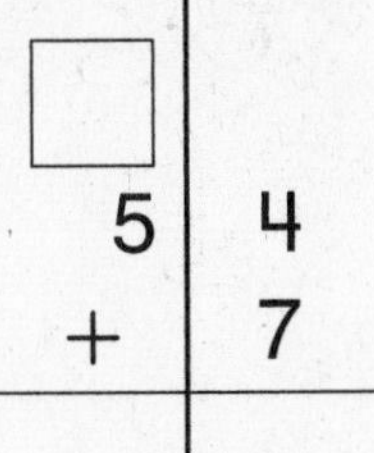

[ ]	[ ]	[ ]	[ ]
5 4	3 7	2 1	4 5
+ 7	+ 9	+ 9	+ 6
___	___	___	___

3.

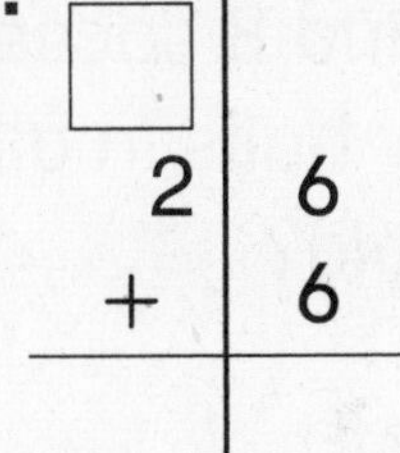

[ ]	[ ]	[ ]	[ ]
2 6	3 5	5 4	7 9
+ 6	+ 7	+ 9	+ 1
___	___	___	___

Solve.

4. Frank has 34 trading cards. He gets 8 more from a friend. How many cards does he have now?

______ cards

5. Ms. Ito has 24 students. 5 new students join her class. How many students does Ms. Ito have in all?

______ students

6. Look at all the problems above. Circle the sums in which you regrouped ones as tens.

Name ______________________________

5-5

Problem-Solving Practice

2AF1.0, 2MR1.2

Add One-Digit Numbers and Two-Digit Numbers

Solve. Regroup if you need to.

1. Fran teaches 12 children to swim on Saturday mornings. She teaches 8 teens to swim on Saturday afternoons. How many people does she teach to swim each Saturday?

_____ people

2. Harry coaches 25 children in basketball on Wednesdays. On Saturday, he coaches 9 more children. How many children does he coach in all?

_____ children

3. The vending machine has 43 cans of orange juice and 9 cans of apple juice. How many total cans of juice are there?

_____ cans

4. The ball rack holds 32 basketballs and 8 soccer balls. How many balls in all does the rack hold?

_____ balls

5. The dodgeball club has fifteen members. Seven new members join. How many members does the club have now?

_____ members

6. Fifty-four people came early to the Tigers' last game. Nine people arrived late and could not find a seat. How many people came to the game?

_____ people

Name ______________________________

5-6

Homework Practice

2NS2.2, 2AF1.3

Add Two-Digit Numbers

Preparation: Base-ten cubes and unit cubes are needed for this activity.

Use WorkMat 6 and [base-ten rod] to add.

1.

1	
3	5
+ 2	5
6	0

4	8
+	8

1	5
+ 5	9

2	9
+ 1	8

2.

5	6
+ 3	5

2	7
+ 2	8

1	4
+ 3	3

3	7
+ 4	6

3.

2	3
+	8

5	4
+ 2	2

4	6
+ 1	9

1	9
+ 3	4

Solve.

4. Jenny sells 32 cups of lemonade. Bruce sells 17 cups. How many cups do they sell together?

______ cups

5. Mr. William's class sells 45 raffle tickets. Ms. Ling's class sells 40. How many tickets do they sell in all?

______ tickets

5-6

Name ______________________________

Problem-Solving Practice

2NS2.2, 2AF1.3

Add Two-Digit Numbers

Solve.

1. This morning Irene paints for 25 minutes. This afternoon she paints for 37 minutes. Write a number sentence to show how many total minutes she paints.

   ______ + ______ = ______

   ______ minutes

2. Mr. Aziz drives his delivery truck 53 miles on Wednesday. On Friday, he drives 34 miles. How many miles did he drive in all?

   ______ + ______ = ______

   ______ minutes

3. Brad's family picks 22 pounds of cherries at home. Then they pick 43 pounds at the orchard. How many pounds of cherries did they pick in all?

   ______ pounds

4. Mr. Cruz's cows gave 48 gallons of milk this morning. This afternoon, they give only 34 gallons. How many gallons of milk did Mr. Cruz's cows give in all?

   ______ gallons

5. Sara picks 24 apples. Her brother picks 33 apples. How many apples do they pick altogether?

   ______ apples

   Their mom needs 21 apples to bake a pie. Can she bake two pies? Explain.

   ____

   ____

6. Sandy wants to buy a pen. It costs 87 cents. She has 7 dimes and 26 pennies. Can she buy the pen? Prove your answer.

   ____

   ____

Name ______________________________

5-7

Homework Practice

2NS6.0, 2NS2.0

Estimate Sums

Chapter Resources

Add. Then round each addend to the nearest ten. Estimate the sum.

1. 54 → 50 + 15 → + 20 69 70	**2.** 34 + 37 + ____	**3.** 24 + 19 + ____
4. 17 + 17 + ____	**5.** 58 + 29 + ____	**6.** 32 + 41 + ____
7. 48 + 26 + ____	**8.** 29 + 14 + ____	**9.** 67 + 22 + ____
10. 16 + 67 + ____	**11.** 46 + 19 + ____	**12.** 37 + 27 + ____

Solve.

13. There are 34 adults at the Swim Club. There are 57 children at the Swim Club. About how many people are at the Swim Club?

about ______ people

14. There are 24 apples in the first basket. There are 37 apples in the second basket. About how many apples are there total?

about ______ apples

Name ____________________

5-7

Problem-Solving Practice

2NS6.0, 2NS2.0

Estimate Sums

Solve. Use the number line to help you round the addends.

1. Sam's puppy has 11 spots. Mo's puppy has 18 spots. About how many spots are there altogether?

   about 10 + about 20 = about ______ spots

2. Sam counts 16 birds on a fence and 28 birds in a tree. About how many birds does Sam count?

   about ______ + about ______ = about ______ birds

3. The toy store has 47 dolls near the front door. There are 36 dolls in the back of the store. About how many dolls does the store have to sell?

   about ______ dolls

4. Vikki has 34 cans for recycling. Monica has 38 cans for recycling. About how many cans will they recycle together?

   about ______ cans

5. Hal reads a book for forty-three minutes. Then he reads another book for forty-six minutes. About how many minutes does Hal spend reading?

   about ______ minutes

6. Jack's trail mix has forty-five peanuts. It also has fifty-two walnuts. About how many nuts are in the trail mix?

   about ______ nuts

Name ______________________________

5-8

Homework Practice

2AF1.1, 2MR3.0

Add Three Two-Digit Numbers

1.

1 26	52	23	71	53
45	23	33	14	27
+ 24	+ 18	+ 43	+ 13	+ 10
95				

2.

11	39	47	38	36
19	51	36	34	24
+ 24	+ 0	+ 16	+ 20	+ 32

3.

71	35	44	39	28
13	27	22	38	25
+ 15	+ 15	+ 26	+ 11	+ 35

Solve.

4. The Tan family is going apple picking. Mr. Tan picks 24 apples. Mrs. Tan picks 35 apples. Their son picks 26 apples. How many apples do the Tans pick?

______ apples

5. Look back over this page. Choose one problem. In the space below, write a story problem for the sum.

____

____

____

____

Name ______________________________

5-8

Problem-Solving Practice

2AF1.1, 2MR3.0

Add Three Two-Digit Numbers

Solve. Make a 10 or use doubles to help you add.

1. The zoo is open 10 hours on Fridays, 12 hours on Saturdays, and 8 hours on Sundays. How many hours is it open during those three days?

______ hours

2. The bear cub takes a 15-minute nap. Later, she takes a second nap for 23 minutes. Her last nap is 25 minutes. How much time does the cub spend napping?

______ minutes

3. Three monkeys weigh 51 pounds. One weighs 12 pounds and another weighs 21 pounds. How much does the third monkey weigh?

______ pounds

4. Dr. Shu takes care of 24 birds. She takes care of some cubs and 13 pups. She takes care of 55 animals in all. How many were cubs?

______ cubs

Number of Zoo Visitors			
Visitor	Friday	Saturday	Sunday
Children	15	22	19
Adults	8	15	13

5. How many children visited the zoo in all?

______ children

6. How many adults visited the zoo in all?

______ adults

Name ______________________________

5-9

Homework Practice

2MR1.1, 2AF1.2

Problem-Solving Investigation: Choose a Strategy

Chapter Resources

Problem-Solving Strategies
- Draw a Picture
- Work Backward
- Write a Number Sentence

Solve.

1. Madge, Sierra, and Tyra baked pies for the state fair. Madge's pie did not come in second. The judges like Sierra's pie better than Madge's. Sierra came in second. Whose pie won first place?

   ________ pie won first place.

2. Mr. Green judged 24 cows. He judged twice as many horses as cows. How many cows and horses did he judge in all?

   ______ cows and horses

3. The fair has a pumpkin contest. The biggest pumpkin weighs 37 pounds. The second-place pumpkin weighs 36 pounds. A 26-pound pumpkin wins third. How much do the three pumpkins weigh in all?

   ______ pounds

4. Thirty people watch the dog show on Wednesday. On Thursday, four more people watch the dogs than on Wednesday. On Friday, the number of people who watch the dogs is the same as the number who watch on Thursday. How many people watch the dog show on Friday?

   ______ people

Name ______________________________

6-1

Homework Practice

2MR3.0, 2NS2.3

Subtract Tens

Subtract tens.

1. 7 tens − 3 tens = ______ tens

$$\begin{array}{r} 70 \\ -\ 30 \\ \hline \end{array}$$

5 tens − 2 tens = ______ tens

$$\begin{array}{r} 50 \\ -\ 20 \\ \hline \end{array}$$

2. $\begin{array}{r} 80 \\ -\ 40 \\ \hline \end{array}$ $\begin{array}{r} 90 \\ -\ 20 \\ \hline \end{array}$ $\begin{array}{r} 40 \\ -\ 30 \\ \hline \end{array}$ $\begin{array}{r} 90 \\ -\ 70 \\ \hline \end{array}$

3. $\begin{array}{r} 80 \\ -\ 50 \\ \hline \end{array}$ $\begin{array}{r} 40 \\ -\ 20 \\ \hline \end{array}$ $\begin{array}{r} 80 \\ -\ 60 \\ \hline \end{array}$ $\begin{array}{r} 70 \\ -\ 20 \\ \hline \end{array}$

4. $\begin{array}{r} 50 \\ -\ 10 \\ \hline \end{array}$ $\begin{array}{r} 70 \\ -\ 10 \\ \hline \end{array}$ $\begin{array}{r} 60 \\ -\ 30 \\ \hline \end{array}$ $\begin{array}{r} 90 \\ -\ 50 \\ \hline \end{array}$

5. $\begin{array}{r} 90 \\ -\ 80 \\ \hline \end{array}$ $\begin{array}{r} 70 \\ -\ 50 \\ \hline \end{array}$ $\begin{array}{r} 80 \\ -\ 10 \\ \hline \end{array}$ $\begin{array}{r} 50 \\ -\ 30 \\ \hline \end{array}$

Solve.

6. Josie has 6 dimes. She spends 3 of the dimes. How much money does Josie have left?

_____ ¢ − _____ ¢ = _____ ¢

7. Rich has eight dimes. He spends four. How much money does Rich have now?

_____ ¢ − _____ ¢ = _____ ¢

Name ______________________________

6-1

Problem-Solving Practice

2MR3.0, 2NS2.3

Subtract Tens

Solve.

1. What is 2 tens from 3 tens? ______ – ______ = ______

2. What is 5 tens from 9 tens? ______

3. What is 1 ten from 3 tens? ______ – ______ = ______.

4. What is 4 tens from 8 tens? ______

5. Dee has nine dimes. She spent seven of them at the mall. How much money does she have now?

______¢

6. Larry has six dimes. He spent half of them at the movies. How much money does he have left?

______¢

7. Jill had 8 dimes. She spent 5 of the dimes. How much money does she have now?

____

8. Andy had ten dimes. He spent half of them on a neat pencil. How much money does Andy have now?

____

9. Jane had some dimes. She spent 4 dimes. Then she had 5 dimes left. How many dimes did Jane have to start with?

____

____

10. Bill had nine dimes. He spent 2 dimes at the mall and 4 dimes at the movies. How many dimes does Bill have left?

____

____

6-2

Name ______________________________

Homework Practice

2AF1.0

Count Back Tens and Ones

Count back to subtract.

1.	85 − 30	38 − 6	57 − 20	42 − 20	97 − 4
2.	74 − 50	37 − 30	86 − 2	27 − 6	79 − 40
3.	53 − 10	68 − 5	43 − 30	83 − 50	34 − 3
4.	22 − 2	57 − 20	68 − 50	75 − 2	89 − 40

Solve.

5. Mandy had three dimes and seven pennies. She spends five pennies at the store. How much money does she have left?

______ ¢

6. Vernon had 38 apples. He gave 20 to his friends. How many apples did he have left? ______ apples

7. What is 5 tens from 9 tens? ______ − ______ = ______

8. What is 2 tens from 8 tens? ______ − ______ = ______

6-2

Name ______________________________

Problem-Solving Practice

2AF1.0

Count Back Tens and Ones

Solve.

1. June has 14 baseball cards. She gives two to a friend. How many cards are left?

______ cards

2. Donald has 56 grapes. He eats five of them. How many grapes does he have left?

______ grapes

3. Billy has 24 marbles. He loses eight of them. How many marbles does he have left?

______ marbles

4. Tricia has 18 stamps. She gives ten to her sister. How many stamps are left?

______ stamps

5. Dr. Miller has 79 patients in one week. 30 are children. The rest are adults. How many adults does Dr. Miller see?

______ adults

6. Tanya collects 185 cans. She crushes 50 cans. How many cans does she have left to crush?

______ cans

Name ______________________________

6-3

Homework Practice

2AF1.0, 2MR1.2

Regroup Tens as Ones

Chapter Resources

Use WorkMat 6 and [tens rod] to subtract.

	Do you need more ones to subtract?	Write the difference.
1. 54 – 6	no yes	54 – 6 = ______
2. 32 – 7	no yes	32 – 7 = ______
3. 82 – 8	no yes	82 – 8 = ______
4. 47 – 5	no yes	47 – 5 = ______
5. 63 – 6	no yes	63 – 6 = ______
6. 91 – 3	no yes	91 – 3 = ______

Solve.

7. Sam picks 41 plums. He eats three for his snack. How many plums are left?

______ plums

8. Mr. White is 54 years old. Mr. Martin is 7 years younger than Mr. White. How old is Mr. Martin?

______ years old

Name ______________________________

6-3

Problem-Solving Practice

2AF1.0, 2MR1.2

Regroup Tens as Ones

Preparation: Base-ten blocks are needed for this activity.

Solve. Use blocks or the tens and ones workmat for help.

1. Melissa makes 14 cards. She gives 7 to her friends.

   How many cards are left?

   ______ cards

2. Joe has 53 coins. He gives 8 to his mom.

   How many coins does he have left?

   ______ coins

3. Fran has a lemonade stand with 81 glasses of lemonade. She sells 9 of them.

   How many glasses are left?

   ______ glasses

4. Vicki has 22 barrettes. She loses 4.

   How many are left?

   ______ barrettes

5. Main Street Store has 38 coats. Nine are sold.

   How many coats are left to sell?

   ______ coats

6. Andy had 44 CDs. He broke 5 of them. Then he sold nine to his friends.

   How many CDs does he have now?

   ______ CDs

Name ______________________________

6-4

Homework Practice

2AF1.2, 2MR1.0

Problem-Solving Strategy: Write a Number Sentence

Write a number sentence to solve.

1. The store has 15 sandwiches. Six are sold. How many sandwiches are left to sell?

   ______ ◯ ______ ◯

   ______ sandwiches

2. Timmy the turtle moves 14 inches. Then he moves three inches. How many inches did he move in all?

   ______ ◯ ______ ◯

   ______ inches

3. There are 12 pinecones in the tree. Two fall off. How many pinecones are left on the tree?

   ______ ◯ ______ ◯

   ______ pinecones

4. There are nine gophers in the garden. There are ten more in the yard. How many gophers are there?

   ______ ◯ ______ ◯

   ______ gophers

5. Gary makes 16 hotdogs. He sells 11. How many hot dogs are left?

   ______ ◯ ______ ◯

   ______ hotdogs

6. There are 11 kites in the sky. There are two more in the tree.

   How many kites are there in all?

   ______ ◯ ______ ◯

   ______ kites

Name ______________________________

6-5

Homework Practice

2AF1.0, 2MR2.1

Subtract One-Digit Numbers from Two-Digit Numbers

Use WorkMat 6 and [ten-rod] to subtract.

1.

tens	ones
☐	☐
5	5
–	7

tens	ones
☐	☐
8	3
–	5

tens	ones
☐	☐
3	6
–	9

tens	ones
☐	☐
9	0
–	8

2.

tens	ones
☐	☐
4	3
–	1

tens	ones
☐	☐
6	2
–	8

tens	ones
☐	☐
7	8
–	9

tens	ones
☐	☐
9	1
–	4

3. There are 23 children playing outside. 7 go inside. How many are left outside?

______ children

4. Karen has 35 grapes. She gives eight to her friends. How many grapes are left?

______ grapes

Name ______________________________

6-5

Problem-Solving Practice

2AF1.0, 2MR2.1

Subtract One-Digit Numbers from Two-Digit Numbers

Solve.

1. Juan has 15 crackers. He eats 4. How many are left?

_____ crackers

2. Rita has 22 stickers. She gives five to Paul. How many stickers are left?

_____ stickers

3. Julia has 24 cards. She trades six cards for a book. How many cards does she have left?

_____ cards

4. Lisa has 18 raisins. She eats 6. How many are left?

_____ raisins

5. Jessie has 34 marbles. He loses seven of them. How many does he have now?

_____ marbles

6. There are 82 balls in the gym. Sam puts nine away. How many balls are still in the gym?

_____ balls

Name ______________________________

6-6

Homework Practice

2AF1.0, 2NS2.0

Subtract Two-Digit Numbers

Use WorkMat 6 and [ten-rod] to subtract.

1.

tens	ones
☐	☐
4	3
– 2	5

tens	ones
☐	☐
6	7
– 2	8

tens	ones
☐	☐
3	5
– 1	9

2.

tens	ones
☐	☐
4	8
– 3	7

tens	ones
☐	☐
8	2
– 5	6

tens	ones
☐	☐
5	6
– 2	8

3. Tom did his chores in 38 minutes. Linda did her chores in 29 minutes. How many more minutes did it take Tom to do his chores?

______ minutes

4. There were 75 straws in the lunchroom. Kids used 27 of them at lunchtime. How many straws were left?

______ straws.

5. Main Street Store has 71 comic books. Five of them are sold. How many comic books are there now?

______ comic books

6. There are 25 students in Miss Fuentes's second grade. There are six students absent today. How many students are there in class today?

______ students.

Name ______________________________

6-6

Problem-Solving Practice

2AF1.0, 2NS2.0

Subtract Two-Digit Numbers

Solve.

1. Ray has 56 comics. He gives 13 away. How many are left?

   ______ comics

2. Jake collects 62 game cards. He gives 48 to a friend. How many cards does Jake have left?

   ______ cards

3. Vera has 21 stamps. Meg has nine stamps. How many more stamps does Vera have?

   ______ more stamps

4. Robbie Rabbit dug up 37 carrots. He ate 33. How many are left?

   ______ carrots

5. There are 31 days in August. There are 28 days in February. How many more days are there in August?

   ______ more days

6. John has 15 points. Ella has six points. Felix has eight points. How many more points does John have than Ella?

   ______ more points

Name ______________________________

6-7

Homework Practice

2NS2.1, 2MR2.2

Check Subtraction

Subtract. Then check by adding.

1.

37		67		52	
− 15	+ ____	− 48	+ ____	− 36	+ ____

2.

48		73		82	
− 18	+ ____	− 7	+ ____	− 68	+ ____

3.

91		35		77	
− 45	+ ____	− 17	+ ____	− 41	+ ____

Solve. Check by adding.

4. There are 46 girls skating. There are 67 boys skating. How many more boys than girls are skating?

______ more boys

5. Randy checks out 20 books from the library. He returns 12. How many books does Randy still have?

______ books

Name ______________________________

6-7

Problem-Solving Practice

2NS2.1, 2MR2.2

Check Subtraction

Solve. Check by adding.

1. Cole has 9 stickers. He gave 2 to a friend. How many stickers does Cole have now?

   ______ stickers

2. Nan's Bike Shop fixed 37 bikes in a week. Ben's Bikes fixed 14. How many more bikes were fixed at Nan's?

   ______ bikes

3. There are 95 cats at the shelter. 28 cats are adopted. How many cats are still at the shelter?

   ______ cats

4. The hen lays 8 eggs. The farmer takes 3. How many are left?

   ______ eggs

5. Ima picks 48 apples. She sells 17 of them. How many apples are left?

   ______ apples

6. Marvin plants 66 flowers. Roy plants 81 flowers. How many more flowers did Roy plant?

   ______ more flowers

Name ______________________________

Homework Practice

2MR1.1, 2AF1.0

Problem-Solving Investigation: Choose a Strategy

- Write a number sentence.
- Draw a picture.
- Use a model.

Choose a strategy and solve.

1. Todd eats 12 crackers. Then he eats 6 more.
How many crackers did he eat?

______ crackers

2. Ms. Allen paints 19 pictures of the prairie.
She paints 37 pictures of her parrot.
How many more pictures of her parrot did she paint?

______ more pictures of her parrot

3. Mary brings four cents to school.
She finds five more in her desk.
Then a friend gives her 13 cents.
How much does Mary have now?

______ cents

4. Mr. Drew teaches reading. He read
3 stories to his students in the first week.
He read 2 stories the next week.
He read 4 stories the week after that.
How many stories has he read so far?

______ stories

Name ______________________________

Homework Practice

2NS2.0, 2NS2.3

Estimate Differences

Round each number to the nearest ten.
Estimate the difference.

1. 74 − 16

− ______

2. 54 − 17

− ______

3. 76 − 27

− ______

4. 38 − 29

− ______

5. 64 − 16

− ______

6. 63 − 21

− ______

Solve.

7. A farmer has 72 apples. She sells 39 of them. About how many apples are left?

______ apples

8. Ray's Bookstore has 92 books about cars. Over a year, 26 books are sold. About how many books on cars are still at the store?

______ books

Name ______________________________

6-9

Problem-Solving Practice

2NS2.0, 2NS2.3

Estimate Differences

Solve.

1. Janet has 21 cents. She spends 9. About how much is left?

   ______ cents

2. Kim has 54 marbles. 19 of them are red. The rest are blue. About how many marbles are blue?

   ______ marbles

3. Mr. Tam's Shop had 91 cans of juice. The store sold 75 in a week. About how many cans of juice are still for sale?

   ______ cans of juice

4. Tim has 12 pencils. He gives 1 to a friend. About how many are left?

   ______ pencils

5. Erin collects 88 cans. She crushes 59 of them. About how many cans are left to crush?

   ______ cans

6. Peter is 50 inches tall. His younger sister is 19 inches shorter than Peter. About how tall is Peter's sister?

   ______ inches

Name ___

7-1

Homework Practice

2NS5.0

Pennies, Nickels, and Dimes

Skip count to find the value. Write the values.

1.         

___¢ ___¢ ___¢ ___¢ ___¢ ___¢ ___¢ ___¢ ___¢

Total ___¢

2.   

___¢ ___¢ ___¢ Total ___¢

3.       

___¢ ___¢ ___¢ ___¢ ___¢ ___¢ ___¢ Total ___¢

4.         

___¢ ___¢ ___¢ ___¢ ___¢ ___¢ ___¢ ___¢

Total ___¢

Solve.

5. Mr. Chau sells hats for 80¢. Willy would like to buy one. How many dimes does Willy need? ___

6. Phil has six dimes. Joan has nine nickels. Who has more money? ___

7. Look back over the page. Circle the answer that is equal to 4 dimes.

Name ____________________

7-1

Problem-Solving Practice

2NS5.0

Pennies, Nickels, and Dimes

Solve.

1. Linda has eight nickels. How much money does Linda have?

   ______¢

2. Manuel has two dimes and three nickels. How much money does he have?

   ______¢

3. Emma has six dimes and four nickels. Kites cost 80¢. Does Emma have enough money to buy a kite? ______

4. Cassie has four nickels. How much money does she have? ______¢

5. Cindy has seven dimes and four pennies. How much money does she have?

   ______¢

6. Yo-yos cost 97¢. Derrick has five dimes, four nickels, and eight pennies. Does Derrick have enough money to buy a yo-yo?

   ______

7. Peter has 7 coins. Five of the coins are pennies. The rest are dimes. How much money does Peter have?

   ______¢

8. Cam has 2 pennies, 6 nickels, and 3 dimes. Does he have enough to buy a snack for 55¢?

   ______

Name ______________________________

7-2

Homework Practice

2NS5.0, 2MR1.2

Quarters and Half-Dollars

Count the value of the coins. Use coins to help.
Then write the total in the price tag.

1.   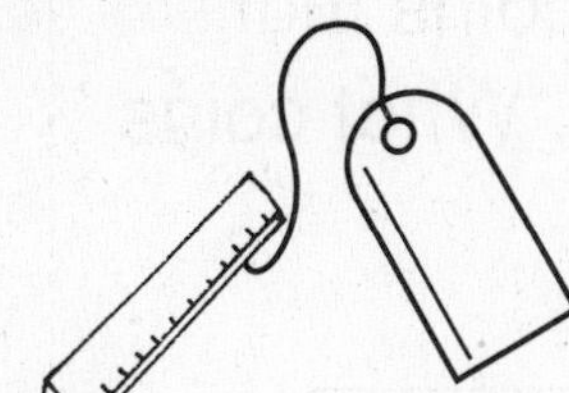

______¢ ______¢ ______¢

2.      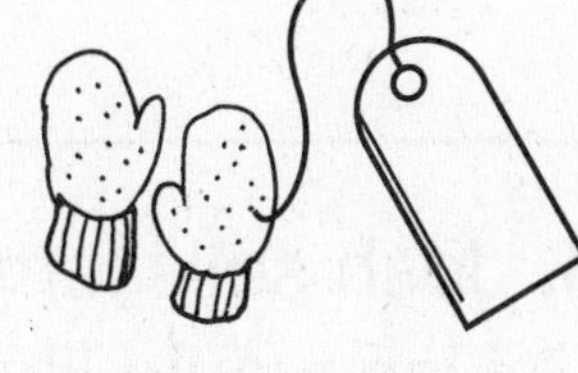

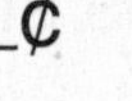 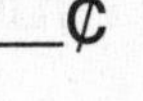 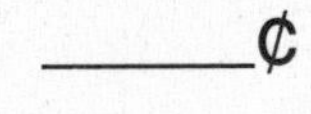 

______¢ ______¢ ______¢ ______¢ ______¢

3.         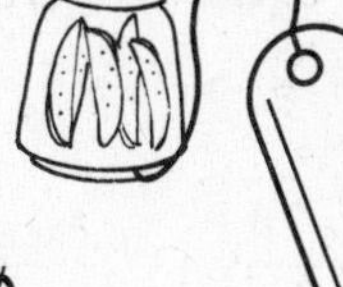

______¢ ______¢ ______¢ ______¢ ______¢ ______¢ ______¢

4.    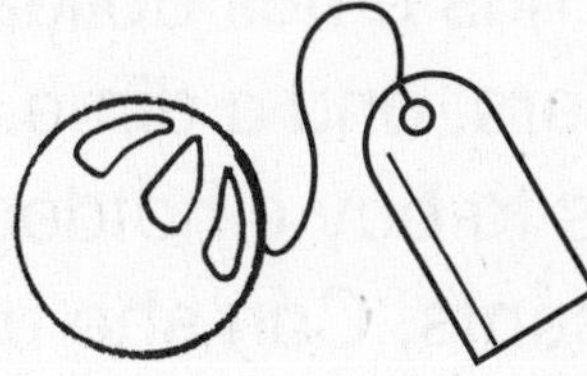

______¢ ______¢ ______¢ ______¢

Solve.

5. Frank has eight quarters in his pocket. How much money does he have? ______¢

6. Yoko has two quarters. How much money does she have?

______¢

7. Lucy has six dimes. How much money does she have? ______¢

7-2

Name ______________________________

Problem-Solving Practice

2NS5.0

Quarters and Half-Dollars

Solve.

1. Shane has two coins that equal 100 cents. What coins are they?

   ____

2. Kito has 3 coins that equal 80 cents. What coins are they?

   ____

   ____

3. Josh sells lemons for 75¢. Lisa would like to buy one. How many quarters does Lisa need? ______

4. Nicole has two quarters. How much money does she have? ______¢

5. Alice has a half dollar, two quarters, and a dime. She wants to buy a hotdog for 100 cents. Can she buy one? ______

6. Barbara has eight pennies, five nickels, and three dimes. Rick has three quarters. Who has more money? ________

7. Anton has 2 quarters, a dime, and a penny. Can he buy a soda for 75¢?

   ______

8. Leslie has 3 coins that equal 100 cents. Two coins are quarters. What is the other coin?

   ____

Name ______________________________

7-3

Homework Practice

2NS5.0

Count Coins

Chapter Resources

Count to find the total amount.

1.       

_____¢ _____¢ _____¢ _____¢ _____¢ _____¢ _____¢

total _____¢

2.       

_____¢ _____¢ _____¢ _____¢ _____¢ _____¢ _____¢

total _____¢

3.     

_____¢ _____¢ _____¢ _____¢ _____¢

total _____¢

4.        

_____¢ _____¢ _____¢ _____¢ _____¢ _____¢ _____¢

total _____¢

Solve.

5. Tom has six dimes, a nickel, and three pennies. How much does he have? _____¢

6. Mai has a two quarters, a dime, a nickel, and a penny. How much money does she have? _____¢

7. Circle the totals that are greater than one dollar.

Name ______________________________

7-3

Problem-Solving Practice

2NS5.0

Count Coins

Solve.

1. Jean has 3 coins that equal 70¢. What coins are they?

____

____

2. Steven has a quarter, a dime, and five pennies. Tina has three dimes and eight pennies. Who has more money? __________

3. Sally sells flags for 90¢. Renee has a half-dollar, a quarter, and a dime. Can she buy a flag? _____

4. Linda has 4 coins that equal 56 cents. What coins are they?

____

____

5. Marge has two quarters. Joey has six dimes. Who has more money? ________

6. Don wants to buy a beach ball for 65¢. He has two quarters, three pennies, and two dimes. Does Don have enough money to buy the ball? _____.

7. Katie has 4 quarters. Sam has 4 dimes. Who has more money?

____

8. Cory has a quarter and six pennies. How much money does he have?

______

7-4

Name ______

Homework Practice

2NS5.0, 2AF1.2

Problem-Solving Strategy: Act It Out

Preparation: Play money is needed for this activity.

Use coins to act out and solve the problem.

1. John gets 1 quarter for chores each day. How much money does John make in 3 days?

   ______ cents

2. Luke has 3 quarters, 3 nickels, and 6 pennies. Can he buy a toothbrush for 82 cents?

   ______

3. Jean wants a yo-yo that costs 62 cents. She also wants a can of juice that costs 35 cents. How much money does she need to buy both?

   ______ cents

4. Manny has one half dollar and two dimes. How much does he have?

   ______ cents

5. Sabrina has 57 cents. How much more money does Manny have than Sabrina?

   ______ cents

6. Mr.Patel pays Joe 3 quarters each week to rake leaves. How many quarters does Joe have after 3 weeks?

   ______ quarters

Name ______________________

7-5

Homework Practice

2NS4.0, 2NS5.2

Dollar

Count the coins. Write the value.
Circle the coins that make one dollar.

1.      

______¢

2.       

______¢

3.      

______¢

4.       

______¢

Solve.

5. Marty has six dimes, six nickels, and five pennies. A bottle of juice costs one dollar. Does Marty have enough money?

______

6. Order the totals for problems 1–4 from least to greatest.

______¢ ______¢ ______¢ ______¢

Name ______________________________

7-5

Problem-Solving Practice

2NS4.0

Dollar

Solve.

1. Juan has one quarter and one dime. Apples cost one dollar. Does he have enough money to buy an apple? ______

2. Rosa has two quarters, two dimes, one nickel, and five pennies. A bag of nuts costs one dollar. Does Rosa have enough money to buy the nuts? ______

3. A can of juice costs one dollar. Mai has a half-dollar, a quarter, two dimes, and one nickel. Does Mai have enough money to buy juice? ______

4. Erik has a half-dollar and one nickel. It costs one dollar to ride the bumper cars. Does Erik have enough money to ride the bumper cars? ______

5. Maggie has two quarters, four dimes, and ten pennies. Baseballs cost one dollar. Does she have enough money to buy a baseball? ______

6. A beach ball costs one dollar. Sanjay has three quarters, one dime, one nickel, and five pennies. Does he have enough money to buy the beach ball? ______

Name ______________________

7-6

Homework Practice

2NS4.0, 2NS5.2

Dollars and Cents

Chapter Resources

Count the money. Write the amount in dollars and cents.

1.

$ ____.____
dollars cents

2.

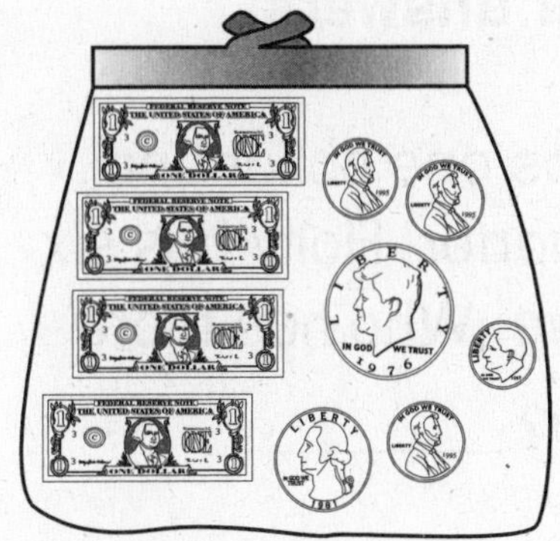

$ ____.____
dollars cents

3.

$ ____.____
dollars cents

4.

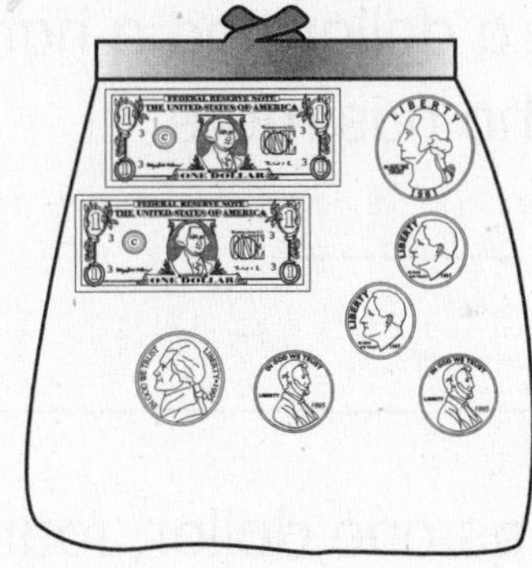

$ ____.____
dollars cents

Solve.

5. Kitty has three dollars, two half-dollars, two quarters, and 12 pennies. How much money does she have?

$ ____.____

6. Lou has two dollars, four quarters, a dime, and three nickels. How much can he spend?

$ ____.____

Name ______

7-6

Problem-Solving Practice

2NS4.0, 2NS5.2

Dollars and Cents

Solve. Use dollar signs and decimal points to write your answers.

1. Rita has one dollar and one quarter. Holly has six quarters. Who has more money? ______

2. Mary has two dollars, four quarters, seven nickels, and two pennies. How much does she have?

   $ ____.____

3. Steve has one quarter, two nickels, a dime, and a dollar. Jake has a dollar and a half dollar. Who has more money? ______

4. David has one dollar and a nickel. How much does he have?

   $ ____.____

5. Brenna has one dollar, four quarters, a dime, and two pennies. She says she has $2.22. Is she right?

   ______

6. Mr. Han has five pennies, two nickels, a quarter, and a dollar. Cartons of milk cost $1.40. Can he buy a carton of milk? ______

7. Jan has 4 nickels and 4 pennies.
   Tom has 1 quarter.
   Who has more money? ______
   How much more? ______

Name ______________________________

7-7 Homework Practice

2NS5.1

Compare Money Amounts

Count. Is there enough money to buy each item? Circle *yes* or *no*.

1. 

yes no

2. 

yes no

3. 

yes no

Solve.

4. Sandy has two dollar bills, one half-dollar, a dime, and nine pennies. The tickets to the fair cost $2.75. Does she have enough to buy a ticket? ______

5. Puppy food costs $4.82. Mr. Burris has three dollar bills, five quarters, five dimes, one nickel, and three pennies. Does he have enough? ______

Name ______________________________

7-7

Problem-Solving Practice

2NS5.1

Compare Money Amounts

Preparation: Play money is needed for this activity.

Solve. Use coins and dollar bills to help.

1. Apples cost 49¢. Felicia has two quarters. Can she buy the apple? ______

2. Garrett has five dollars, a quarter, and three pennies. Movie tickets cost $5.29. Does he have enough money? ______

3. Ruby has four dollars, a half-dollar, and three nickels. Joey has three dollars, five quarters, four dimes, and five pennies. Who has more money? ________

4. Pencils cost $1.05. Joelle has four quarters and a nickel. Can she buy the pencils? ______

5. Dwayne has two dollars, two quarters, nine dimes, and six pennies. A game costs $3.49. Does he have enough money? ______

6. Lenny has three dollars, a dime, and 12 pennies. Lucy has two dollars, a half-dollar, a quarter, two dimes, and five pennies. Who has more money? __________

7. Jason and Kelly both have 45¢. Jason has 3 coins. Kelly has 5 coins. Can this be correct? Prove your answer.

____

____

7-8

Name ______________________________

Homework Practice

2NS2.0, 2NS5.0

Add Money

Chapter Resources

Add.

1. $0.22 + 0.73

2. 54¢ + 29¢

3. 12¢ + 74¢

4. $0.02 + 0.97

5. 6¢ + 48¢

6. $0.21 + 0.26

7. $0.87 + 0.06

8. 50¢ + 39¢

9. 44¢ + 28¢

Solve.

10. Sue had $0.73 in her pocket. Her brother gives her $0.17. How much money does she have? ________

11. Juan has 36¢. Kyle has 17¢. How much money do they have in all? ______

12. Mr. Martin has two dollars, a quarter, and four pennies. A bus ride costs $2.29. Does he have enough to ride the bus? ______

13. Look back over problems 1–6. What is the *range* of the sums?

____

7-8

Name ______________________________

Problem-Solving Practice

2NS2.0, 2NS5.0

Add Money

Solve.

1. Mrs. Gary has $0.10. Leon has $0.80. How much money do they have?

   ____

2. Mandy has 43¢. Kevin has 18¢. How much money do they have altogether? ______

3. Kurt buys a glass of juice for 90¢. Then he buys a sandwich for $1.00. How much money does Kurt spend? ________

4. Wendy has 15¢. Bill has 15¢. How much money do they have altogether? ______

5. Vincent bought a toy car and an eraser. Toy cars cost $0.81. Erasers cost $0.09. How much money did Vincent spend? ________

6. Pencils cost $0.47 each. Angela bought two pencils. How much money did she spend? ________

7. An extra pizza slice at school costs 50¢. What two coins could you use to buy a slice?

   ____

Name ____________________

7-9

Homework Practice

2NS2.0, 2NS5.0

Subtract Money

Chapter Resources

Subtract.

1. $0.71 − $0.37

2. 34¢ − 7¢

3. 81¢ − 18¢

4. $0.89 − $0.33

5. 81¢ − 5¢

6. $2.11 − $1.99

7. $0.87 − 0.06

8. 50¢ − 39¢

9. 44¢ − 28¢

Solve.

10. Betty had $0.87. She spends $0.25 for lunch. Subtract to find out how much money she has left. ______

11. Anna has $0.92. She spends $0.48 at a music store. How much money does she have left? ______

12. Phil has 73¢. He buys an apple for 59¢. How much money does he have left? ______

13. Molly has 78¢. Larry has 87¢. Who has more money? ______ How much more? ______

7-9

Name ________________________________

Problem-Solving Practice

2NS2.0, 2NS5.0

Subtract Money

Solve.

1. Kelly had 89¢. She bought a pack of baseball cards for 55¢. How much money does she have now? ______

2. David has 92¢. Mark has 40¢. How much more money does David have than Mark? ______

3. Mr. Engle had $0.54. The pen he bought costs $0.42. How much money does he have now? _______

4. Carrots cost $0.83. Stephen has 90 cents. He buys carrots. How much money does he have left? _______

5. Pencils cost $0.08. Ken had $0.74. How much money does he have after buying a pencil? _______

6. Wanda has 82¢. Mary has 27¢. How much more money does Wanda have than Mary? ______

7. Doug spent 6¢. He had 45¢. Doug says he has 38 cents left now. Is he right? ______

8. Jean had $0.29. She spent 7¢. How much money does she have now? _______

7-10

Name ______________________________

Homework Practice

2NS5.0, 2MR1.1

Problem-Solving Investigation: Choose a Strategy

Choose a strategy and solve.

Problem-Solving Strategy

- Act It Out
- Choose an Operation
- Guess and Check
- Draw a Picture

1. David had $3.56. He bought a rollercoaster ticket for $1.17.
   How much money does he have now? _______

2. Can David buy another ticket with the money he has left?
   _____

3. Shelly has a row of nine dimes. She took out every other dime and puts down a nickel. Then she picks up every third dime (of the ones left) and puts down a quarter. How much money does Shelly have now? _____

4. A ring toss ticket costs $0.65. A go-cart ticket costs $1.59. A glass of lemonade costs $1.04. How much do all three cost?
   ____

5. Elena has 25¢. Kelly has 82¢. How much more money does Kelly have? _____

6. Ramon has $2.29. He wants to buy a book. A robot book costs one half-dollar, two quarters, and three pennies. A space book costs five quarters, two half-dollars, and one dime. Circle the book Ramon can buy.

   a robot book　　　　　a space book

Name ______________________________

8-1

Homework Practice

Equal Groups

Skip count. Write how many in all.

1.  

______ ______ ______ ______ ______ in all

2.   

______ ______ ______ in all

Circle the equal groups. Write how many groups.

3. ♩♩♩♩♩♩ ♩♩♩♩♩♩ ♩♩♩♩♩♩ ♩♩♩♩♩♩

______ equal groups

Solve.

4. Maya is using skip counting to see how many music notes are in problem 3. How many notes will she find?

______ notes in all

5. Des wants to know how many feathers and eggs in all. Use the totals from problems 1 and 2 to write a number sentence.

______ feathers + ______ eggs = ______ in all

Name ______________________

8-1

Problem-Solving Practice

2NS3.1, 2MR1.2

Equal Groups

How many dots are on Tara's cards? Skip count.

1. 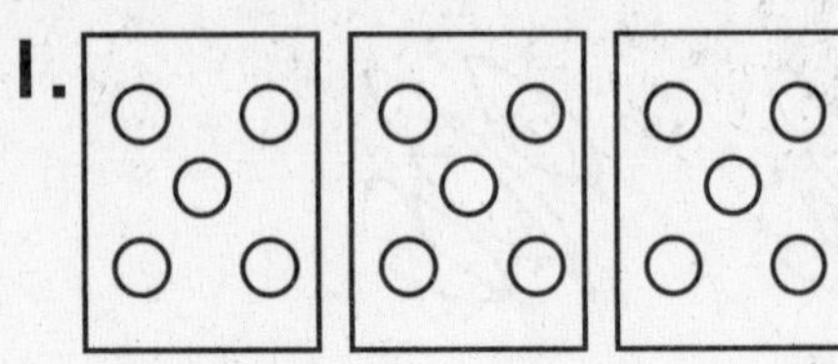

_____ _____ _____

_____ in all

2.

_____ _____ _____

_____ in all

Solve. Draw a picture if you need help.

3. Maria has 12 counters. She puts them into equal groups of 3. How many groups does she make?

_____ groups of 3

4. Gary has 8 counters. He puts them into equal groups of 2. How many groups does he make?

_____ groups of 2

5. Vic has 6 crackers. He wants to put the crackers into equal groups so he can share with friends. Circle all the equal groups that he can make.

2 3 4 5

6. Lin has 12 grapes. She wants to put the grapes into equal groups so that she can share them. Circle all the equal groups that she can make.

2 3 4 5 6

8-2

Name ______________________

Homework Practice

2NS3.1, 2MR3.0

Repeated Addition

Chapter Resources

Add. Then multiply.

1.    

______ + ______ + ______ + ______ = ______

______ × ______ = ______

2.     

______ + ______ + ______ + ______ + ______ = ______

______ × ______ = ______

3. 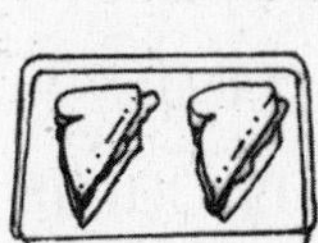  

______ + ______ + ______ = ______

______ × ______ = ______

Solve.

4. Gina's lunch table has 4 trays. Each tray has 2 juice boxes. How many juice boxes are on Gina's table?

______ + ______ + ______ + ______ = ______

______ × ______ = ______

5. Josh's table has 2 trays. Each tray has 5 carrot sticks. How many carrot sticks on Josh's table?

______ + ______ = ______

______ × ______ = ______

8-2

Name ________________

Problem-Solving Practice

2NS3.1, 2MR1.2

Repeated Addition

Write two number sentences to solve.

1. Look at Anne's blocks. How many blocks does she have?

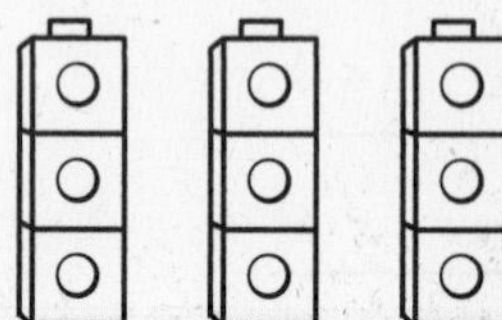

____ + ____ + ____ = ____

____ × ____ = ____

2. How many blocks does Cam have?

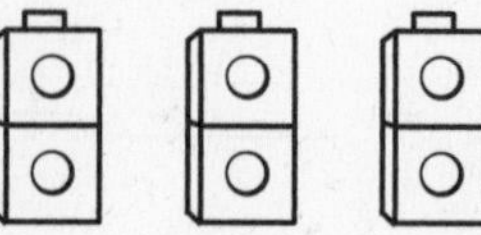

____ + ____ + ____ = ____

____ × ____ = ____

3. Lisa plays with 2 groups of marbles. Each group has 4 marbles. How many marbles does she use?

____ + ____ = ____

____ × ____ = ____

4. Brad makes 4 groups of cards. Each group has 3 cards. How many cards does he make?

____ + ____ + ____ + ____ = ____

____ × ____ = ____

5. Ms. White writes a number sentence.
$2 + 2 + 2 + 2 + 2 =$ ____
What multiplication sentence can she write from the addition sentence?

____ × ____ = ____

6. Mr. Yun writes a number sentence.
$5 + 5 + 5 =$ ____
What multiplication sentence can he write from the addition sentence?

____ × ____ = ____

Name ______________________________

8-3

Homework Practice

2NS3.1, 2MR1.2

Arrays

Chapter Resources

Write a multiplication sentence for each array.

1. 

_____ × _____ = _____

2. _____ × _____ = _____

3. 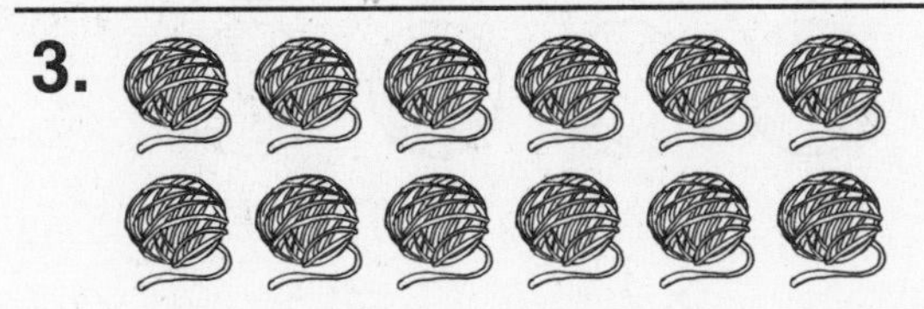

_____ × _____ = _____

4. 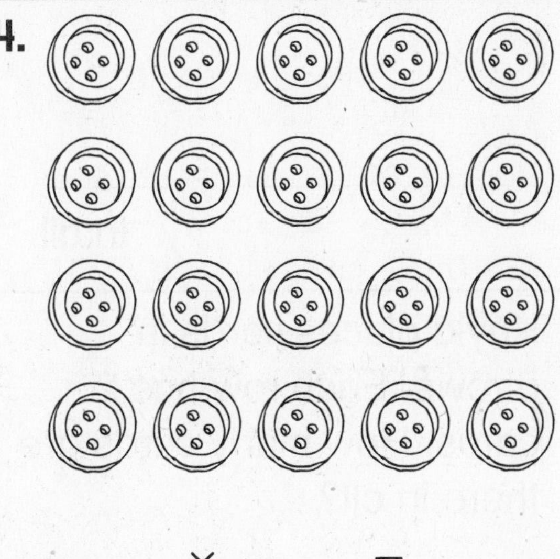

_____ × _____ = _____

Solve. Draw a picture if you need help.

5. Kaya's shirt drawer has 3 rows of shirts. There are 6 shirts in each row. How many shirts does Kaya have?

_____ × _____ = _____

6. Look back over this page. Circle every answer on this page that has a 1 in the tens place.

Name ______________________________

8-3

Problem-Solving Practice

2NS3.1, 2MR1.2

Arrays

Multiply to solve. Draw a picture if you need help.

1. How many balls does Jack have in all? Multiply.

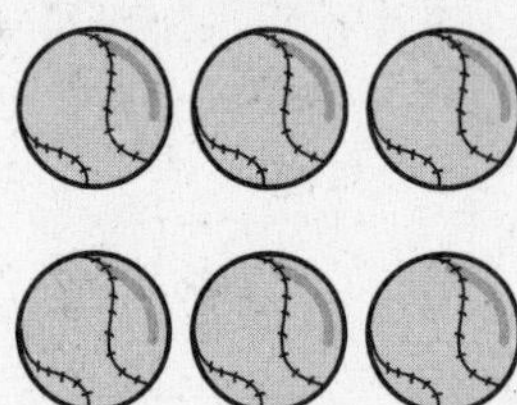

_____ × _____ = _____ in all

2. How many balls does Inez have in all? Multiply.

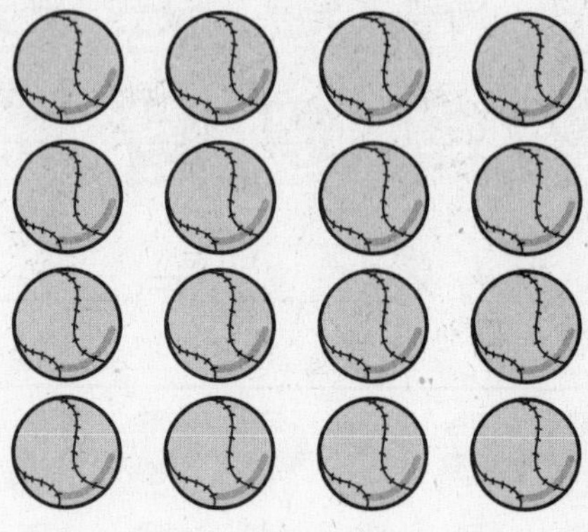

_____ × _____ = _____ in all

3. Kayla places cards in 5 rows. Each row has 2 cards. How many cards are there in all?

_____ × _____ = _____ cards in all

4. Ms. May puts the chairs in 3 rows. She puts 6 chairs in each row. How many chairs does she use?

_____ × _____ = _____ chairs in all

5. Maggie sets up the checker board to play a game. She places 4 checkers in 3 rows. How many checkers does she use?

_____ checkers

6. Pat makes a design on grid paper. He colors 4 rows. Each row has 5 squares. How many squares does he color?

_____ squares

Name ______________________________

8-4

Homework Practice

2NS3.3

Multiply 2s and 5s

Chapter Resources

Multiply.

1. 5 × 8 = ______

2. 2 × 5 = ______

3. 5 × 7 = ______

4. 5 × 3 = ______

5. 5 × 4 = ______

6. 5 × 6 = ______

7. 2 × 9 = ______

8. 3 × 2 = ______

9. 6 × 2 = ______

10. 8 × 2 = ______

11. 4 × 2 = ______

12. 2 × 5 = ______

Multiply to solve.

13. Eli has 7 friends coming to lunch. If each friend eats 2 sandwiches, how many sandwiches should Eli make?

______ × ______ = ______ sandwiches

14. Mia and her family are planning a camping trip. They have 4 tents. Each tent can hold 3 people. How many people can sleep in tents?

______ × ______ = ______ people

15. Dawn has a job walking dogs. She walks 6 groups of dogs each week. There are 2 dogs in each group. How many dogs does Dawn walk each week?

______ × ______ = ______ dogs

Name ______________________

8-4

Problem-Solving Practice

2NS3.3, 2MR3.0

Multiply 2s and 5s

Multiply to solve.

1. Libby is baking 3 pies. Each pie uses 5 apples. How many apples will Libby use in all?

$3 \times 5 =$ ______ apples

2. Joe and Evan each have 6 marbles. How many marbles in all?

$2 \times 6 =$ ______ marbles

3. Cal plants 4 tomato plants. If each plant grows 5 tomatoes, how many tomatoes will Cal have in all?

______ × ______ = ______ tomatoes

4. Yoko buys a pack of erasers. The erasers come in 5 colors. There are 2 erasers for each color. How many erasers does Yoko have?

______ × ______ = ______ erasers

5. Raul has 7 pairs of shoes. There are 2 shoes in each pair. How many single shoes does Raul have?

______ shoes

6. Pamela' s Pet Shop has 6 tanks of goldfish. There are 5 goldfish in each tank. How many goldfish does Pamela have for sale?

______ goldfish

Name ____________________

8-5

Homework Practice

2NS3.0, 2MR1.0

Problem-Solving Strategy: Draw a Picture

Chapter Resources

Draw a picture to solve. **Show your work here.**

1. Lamon, Kit, Ruth, and Dean share a plate of sandwiches. There are 8 sandwiches on the plate. How many sandwiches does each child get?

   ______ sandwiches.

2. Aki needs to pack 18 sweaters into 2 suitcases. How many sweaters in each suitcase?

   ______ sweaters

3. Killian has a bag of 18 dog treats. He feeds the treats to his 3 dogs. How many treats does each dog get?

   ______ treats

4. Rob buys 25 seeds to plant. Seeds come in packets of 5. How many seed packets is Rob buying?

   ______ packets

Name ______

8-6

Homework Practice

2NS3.3

Multiply 10s

Multiply.

1. $10 \times 2 =$ ______

2. $3 \times 10 =$ ______

3. $10 \times 10 =$ ______

4. $10 \times 6 =$ ______

5. $8 \times 10 =$ ______

6. $4 \times 10 =$ ______

7. $10 \times 7 =$ ______

8. $1 \times 10 =$ ______

9. $9 \times 10 =$ ______

10. $10 \times 5 =$ ______

11. $10 \times 3 =$ ______

12. $6 \times 10 =$ ______

13. $7 \times 10 =$ ______

14. $2 \times 10 =$ ______

15. $10 \times 9 =$ ______

Multiply to solve.

16. Sue practiced cello for 10 days in a row. She practiced 1 hour each day. How many hours did Sue practice in all?

______ × ______ = ______ hours

17. Pat is making party favors for his guests. He wants each guest to have 7 party favors. If 10 guests come to Pat's party, how many party favors will he need?

______ × ______ = ______ party favors

18. Frank picked 9 baskets of berries. There were 10 berries in each basket. How many berries did Frank pick in all?

______ × ______ = ______ berries

Name ______________________________

8-6

Problem-Solving Practice

2NS3.3

Multiply 10s

Multiply to solve.

1. Ron has 3 bags. Each bag has 10 apples. How many apples in all?

____ × ____ = ____ apples

2. Elena 10 jars. Each jar has 5 bugs. How many bugs in all?

____ × ____ = ____ bugs

3. Bert and Mark each wrote 10 book reports. How many book reports did they write in all?

____ × ____ = ____ book reports

4. Ellis finished 7 puzzles. Each puzzle had 10 pieces. How many pieces did Ellis use?

____ × ____ = ____ pieces

5. Lauren helped make orange juice for friends. If she gave 10 friends 2 glasses each, how many glasses did Lauren make in all?

____ × ____ = ____ glasses of orange juice

6. Kim's mom built 10 shelves. Kim can fit 10 DVDs on each shelf. How many DVDs will fit in all?

____ × ____ = ____ DVDs

Name ________________________________

8-7

Homework Practice

2NS3.2, 2MR1.2

Repeated Subtraction and Division

Chapter Resources

Preparation: Crayons are needed for this activity.

Put an X on equal groups. Subtract. Then divide.

1. Put an X on groups of 3. How many groups?

_____ ÷ _____ = _____ groups

2. Put an X on groups of 2. How many groups?

_____ ÷ _____ = _____ groups

3. Put an X on groups of 7. How many groups?

_____ ÷ _____ = _____ groups

4. Put an X on groups of 3. How many groups?

_____ ÷ _____ = _____ groups

Solve.

5. Luisa has 21 peas. She puts them into groups of 3. How many groups does Luisa have? Use cubes to solve.

_____ ÷ _____ = _____ groups

6. Look back at problem 4. Color the cubes in an AAAB pattern. Use red and blue. Start with red.

Name ______________________________

8-7

Problem-Solving Practice

2NS3.2, 2MR1.2

Repeated Subtraction and Division

Preparation: A set of connecting cubes is needed for this activity.

Use cubes. Make equal groups.
Subtract. Then divide.

1. There are 9 boxes. Each car has 3 boxes. How many cars?

   9 ÷ 3 = ______

   ______ cars

2. There are 10 bags. Each van has 5 bags. How many vans?

   10 ÷ 5 = ______

   ______ vans

3. Nick has 12 beans. He subtracts groups of 6. How many equal groups of 6 can he make?

   ______ ÷ ______ = ______

   ______ groups

4. Jane has 15 eggs. She subtracts groups of 3. How many equal groups of 3 does she make?

   ______ ÷ ______ = ______

   ______ groups

5. Casey digs up 6 worms. She puts each pair of worms in a jar. How many jars does Casey need?

   ______ jars

6. Mark has 20 rocks. He sorts them by size and puts them in groups of 5. He puts each group in a box. How many boxes does Mark use?

   ______ boxes

Name ______________________________

8-8

Homework Practice

2NS3.2, 2MR1.2

Find Equal Shares

Chapter Resources

Use counters to make equal shares. How many are in each group? Divide.

1. 21 counters
7 equal groups
_____ ÷ _____ = _____

2. 14 counters
2 equal groups
_____ ÷ _____ = _____

3. 18 counters
3 equal groups
_____ ÷ _____ = _____

4. 20 counters
5 equal groups
_____ ÷ _____ = _____

5. 12 counters
3 equal groups
_____ ÷ _____ = _____

6. 30 counters
6 equal groups
_____ ÷ _____ = _____

7. 24 counters
8 equal groups
_____ ÷ _____ = _____

8. 24 counters
4 equal groups
_____ ÷ _____ = _____

Solve.

9. Nina has 16 lizards. The lizards share 4 equal tanks. How many lizards are in each tank?

16 ÷ 4 = _____ lizards

10. Martin had 18 pears. He gave an equal number of pears to 9 friends. How many pears did Martin give to each friend?

18 ÷ 9 = _____ pears

Name ______________________________

8-8

Problem-Solving Practice

2NS3.2, 2MR1.2

Find Equal Shares

Preparation: Counters and extra paper are needed for this activity.

Draw a picture to solve. Use a separate sheet of paper. Use counters if needed.

1. There are 8 bees on bushes. They are in 2 equal groups. How many bees are in each group?

   $8 \div 2 =$ ______

   ______ bees

2. There are 15 bugs on the ground. They are in 5 equal groups. How many bugs in each group?

   $15 \div 5 =$ ______

   ______ bugs

3. Rob has 10 seeds. He puts them into 2 equal groups. How many seeds are in each group?

   $10 \div 2 =$ ______

   ______ seeds

4. Riley has 12 bulbs. She divides them into 3 equal groups. How many bulbs are in each group?

   $12 \div 3 =$ ______

   ______ bulbs

5. Four friends want to share equally the 8 flowers they picked. How many flowers will each friend get?

   ______ flowers

6. Ms. Paul has 18 flowers to plant. She divides the flowers into 6 equal groups. How many flowers are in each group?

   ______ flowers

Name ______________________________

8-9

Homework Practice

2NS3.0, 2MR1.1

Problem-Solving Investigation: Choose a Strategy

Choose a strategy. Solve.

Problem-Solving Strategies
Make a table
Use a model
Draw a picture

1. Grace's farm has 3 lambs.
Each lamb has 4 legs.

How many legs in all?

______ legs

If Grace gets another lamb, how many legs in all?

______ legs

2. Elvin orders 9 CDs.
The CDs come in packs of 3.

How many packs will Elvin get?

______ packs of CDs

---

3. Lucia bought 14 balls of yarn. Each scarf takes 2 balls of yarn to knit.

How many scarves can Lucia knit?

______ scarves

4. Julian made 6 clay pots.
He used 2 blocks of clay for each pot.

How many blocks of clay did he use in all?

______ blocks of clay

Name ______________________________

8-10

Homework Practice

2NS3.2, 2MR1.2

Equal Groups with Remainders

Preparation: Connecting cubes are needed for this activity.

Use cubes to make equal groups. Divide. Write the remainder if there is one.

1. 17 stickers are shared by 4 friends.

17 ÷ 4 = ______ remainder ______

Each friend has ______ stickers, and there is ______ left over.

2. 12 peanuts are shared by 3 parrots.

12 ÷ 3 = ______ remainder ______

Each parrot gets ______ peanuts, and there are ______ peanuts left over.

3. 11 gifts are shared by 5 cousins.

11 ÷ 5 = ______ remainder ______

Each cousin gets ______ gifts, and there is ______ gift left over.

4. Ramón and Fran bought 19 balloons. They shared the balloons equally. Were there any left over? ______

19 ÷ 2 = ______ remainder ______

5. The O'Brien children bought 13 muffins. The 4 children shared the muffins equally. Were there any muffins left over? ______

13 ÷ 4 = ______ remainder ______

Name ______________________________

8-10

Problem-Solving Practice

2NS3.2, 2MR1.2

Equal Groups with Remainders

Preparation: Counting cubes are needed for this activity.

Draw a picture to solve. Use a separate piece of paper. Use cubes if needed.

1. 13 bagels were shared by a family of 6.

   13 ÷ 6 = ______ remainder ______

2. 9 CDs are shared by the 4 Dahl brothers.

   9 ÷ 4 = ______ remainder ______

3. Uri, Ryan, and Sondra made 16 dollars at the sale. They split the money equally. How much money does each friend get?

   ______ ÷ ______ = ______ remainder ______

4. Chris has 17 model airplanes. He put equal groups of model airplanes on 4 shelves. Are there any model airplanes left over? ______

   ______ ÷ ______ = ______ remainder ______

5. Four people shared 9 hotdogs equally. Were there any hotdogs left over? ______

   If so, how many? ______

6. Lin, Wade, Mara, and Jesse bought 22 raffle tickets. They split the tickets equally. Each friend gets ______ tickets. There are ______ tickets left over.

Name ______________________________

9-1

Homework Practice

2NS4.1

Unit Fractions

Chapter Resources

Preparation: Crayons are needed for this activity.

Write the fraction for the shaded part.

1. 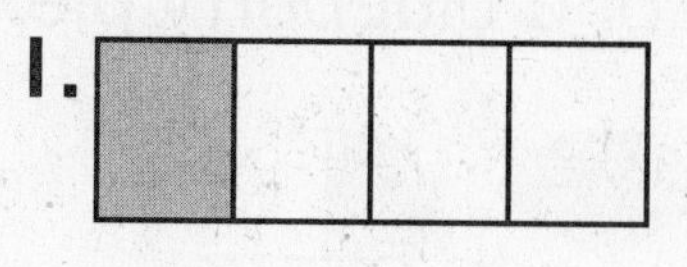

___

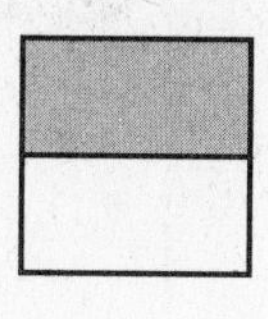

___

___

Color part of each figure to show the fraction.

2. 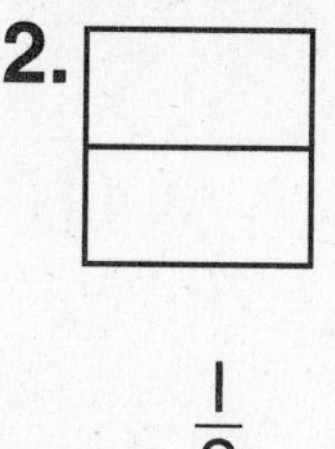

$\frac{1}{2}$

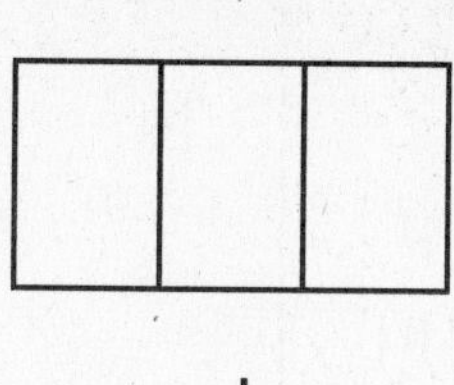

$\frac{1}{3}$

$\frac{1}{8}$

Solve.

3. Jeri cuts a cake into 6 equal slices. She gives 1 slice to her brother. Jeri's brother gets ___ of the cake.

4. Paco's bookcase has 8 equal shelves. He paints 1 shelf blue. Now, his bookcase is ___ blue.

5. Order these numbers from *least* to *greatest*: 64, 12, 46, 24.

_____, _____, _____, _____

9-1

Name ______________________

Problem-Solving Practice

2NS4.1

Unit Fractions

Solve. For 1 and 2, circle the correct picture.
For 3–6, write the answer.

1. Alan ate $\frac{1}{3}$ of a pizza.

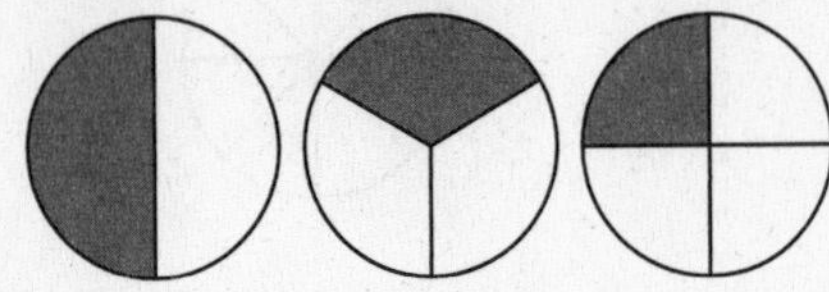

2. Lisa ate $\frac{1}{4}$ of a blueberry pie.

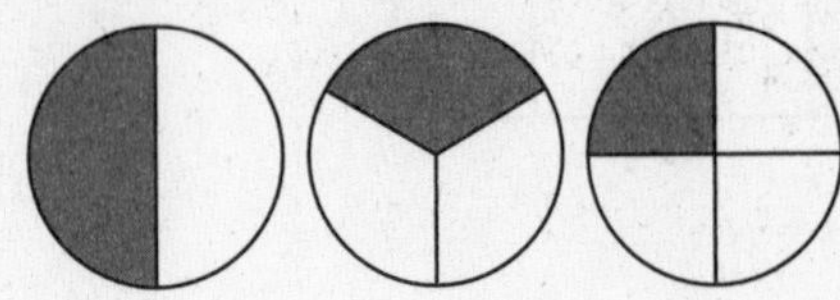

3. How much of the pizza did Frank eat?

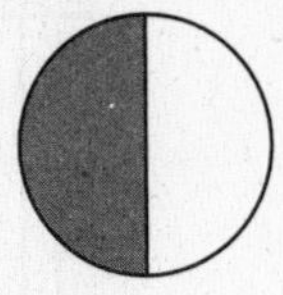

___

4. How much of the pie did Genna eat?

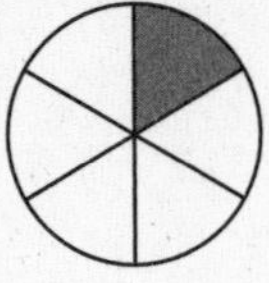

___

5. Jon drew these shapes. Look at each shape and its shaded part. What fraction do Jon's shapes show?

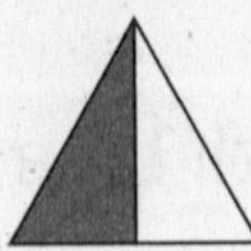
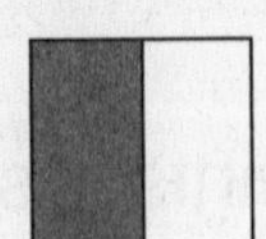
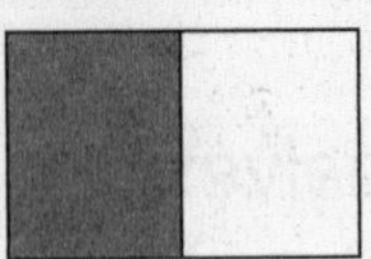

____

6. Sandy says she colored $\frac{2}{3}$ of the circle. Is she right? Explain.

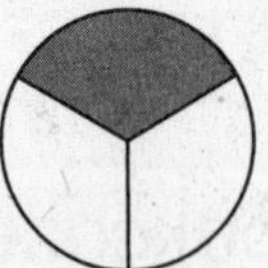

____

9-2

Name ______________________________

Homework Practice

2NS4.0, 2MR1.2

Other Fractions

Preparation: Crayons are needed for this activity.

Write the fraction for the shaded part.

1. 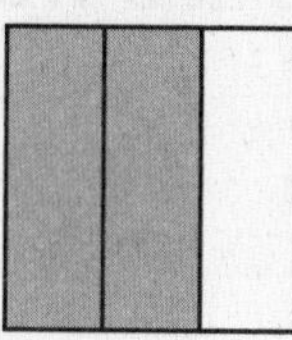

___

2. 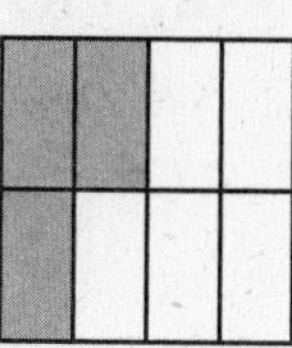

___

3. 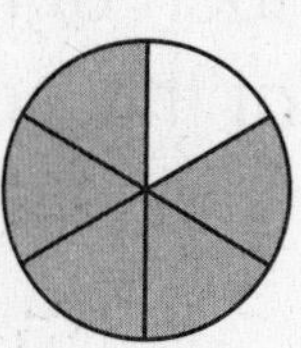

___

Color part of each figure to show the fraction.

4. 

$\frac{2}{8}$

5. 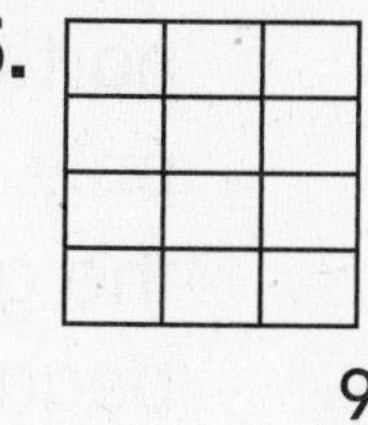

$\frac{9}{12}$

6. 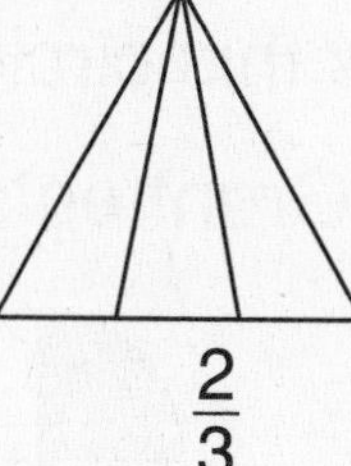

$\frac{2}{3}$

Solve.

7. Lucy's shade is covering nine-twelfths of her window. Draw and color nine-twelfths of a square to show Lucy's window. Write the correct fraction.

___

8. What is the missing number in this pattern?

9, 18, 27, 36, ______, 54

Name ____________________

9-2

Problem-Solving Practice

2NS4.0, 2MR1.2

Other Fractions

Solve. For 1 and 2, circle the correct fraction. For 3–6, write the answer.

1. How much of the cake was eaten at the party?

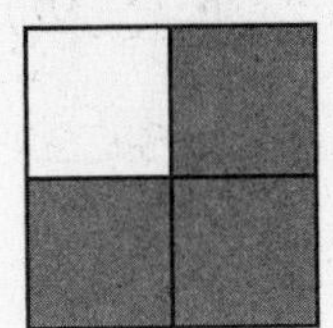

$\frac{2}{4}$ $\frac{3}{4}$ $\frac{4}{4}$

2. How much of the pizza was eaten?

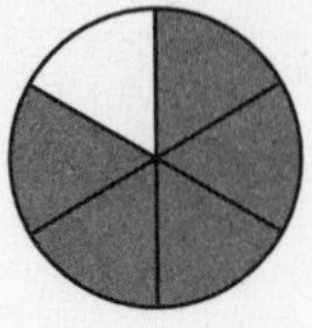

$\frac{2}{6}$ $\frac{4}{6}$ $\frac{5}{6}$

3. Grant eats $\frac{1}{3}$ of a burger. Does this circle show the part Grant eats?

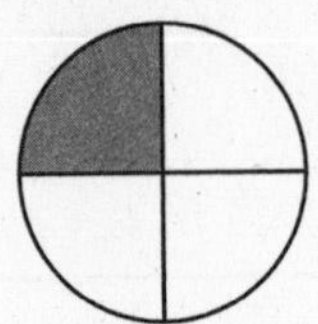

____

4. Naomi's garden has 4 equal parts. She plants beans in only 1 part. What part of the garden does not have beans?

____

5. Kali and James are sharing an orange. Kali eats $\frac{2}{5}$ of the orange. James eats $\frac{3}{5}$ of the orange.
Who eats more?

____

6. Paul ate 2 pieces of pizza. Put a **P** on each piece he ate. Amy ate $\frac{2}{6}$ of the pizza. Put an **A** on each piece she ate.

What fraction is left?

______

Name ___________________________________

9-3

Homework Practice

2NS4.0, 2MR1.0

Problem-Solving Strategy: Draw a Picture

Chapter Resources

Draw a picture to solve. Show your work.

1. Mr. Sun's flower garden has 7 equal parts. He plants tulips and lilies. The tulips are in 4 of the parts. What part of the garden has lilies?

___ of the garden has lilies.

2. Nell's kite looks like a diamond with 4 equal parts. Two of the parts are yellow. What fraction of the kite is yellow?

Nell's kite is ___ yellow.

3. Leah wants to cut a pie into equal pieces to share with five cousins. If Leah also wants some, how many pieces should she cut?

Leah should cut _____ pieces.

Name ________________________________

Homework Practice

2NS4.2, 2NS4.3

Fractions Equal to 1

Preparation: Crayons are needed for this activity.

Count and color all parts of each whole. Then write the fraction for the whole.

1. 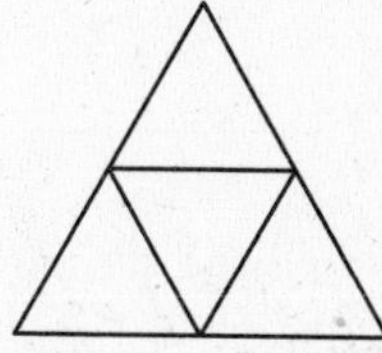

____

2. 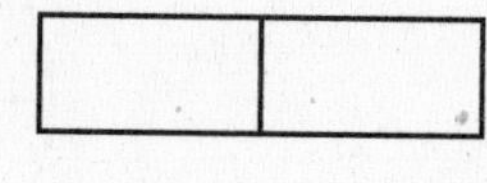

____

3. 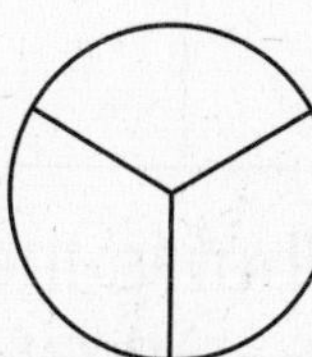

____

4. 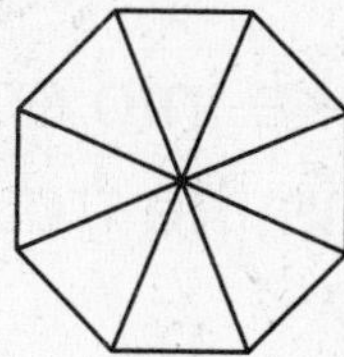

____

5. 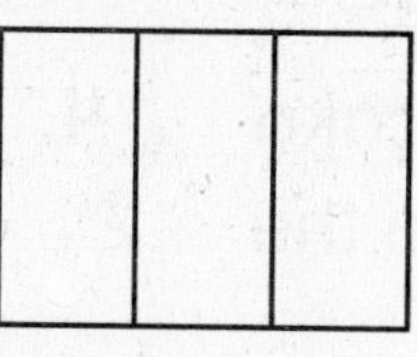

____

6. 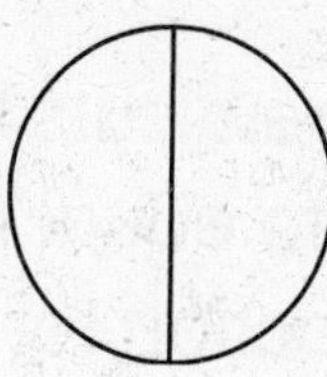

____

Solve

7. Kate cut a pie into 4 equal parts. Color each part of the pie. Next to it, write the fraction for the whole of the pie.

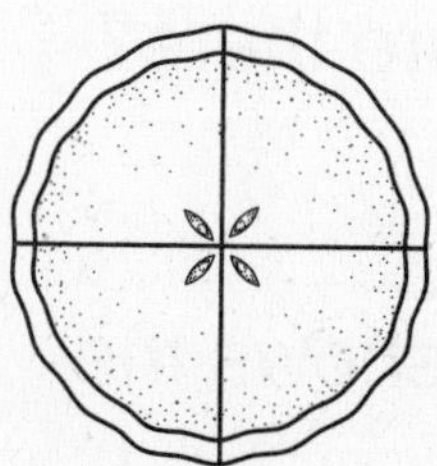

____

8. Circle the numbers in this group that have a 3 in the tens place.

16 11 36 53 34 43 20 24

Name ______________________________

9-4

Problem-Solving Practice

2NS4.2, 2NS4.3

Fractions Equal to 1

Write and circle the correct answers.

1. This is Cam's table.

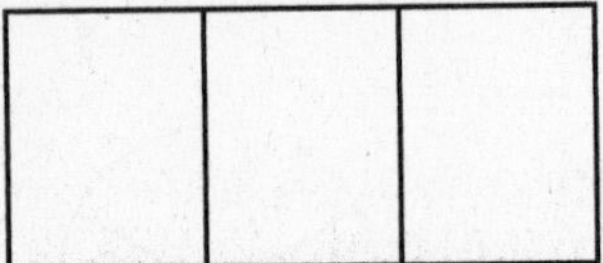

What is the fraction for the whole? Circle it.

$\frac{2}{2}$ $\frac{3}{3}$ $\frac{5}{5}$

2. This is May's window.

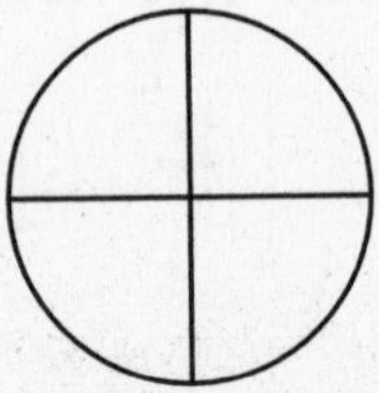

What is the fraction for the whole? ______

3. Drew cuts his birthday cake into equal pieces. Circle the fraction for the whole.

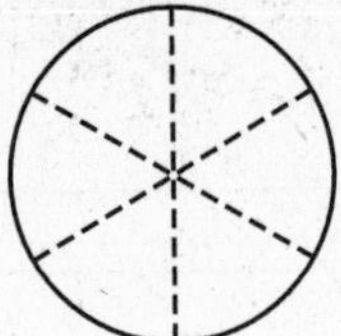

$\frac{3}{3}$ $\frac{6}{6}$ $\frac{8}{8}$

4. Dee cuts a cake into equal pieces. What is the fraction for the whole?

______ 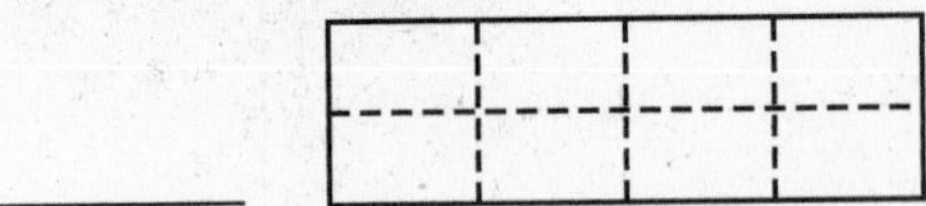

5. Jason bakes a peach pie. He and 5 of his friends will eat it. Into how many equal pieces should he cut the pie?

______

What is the fraction for the whole? ______

6. Lin and Dave are sharing a cookie. If they each have an equal part of the cookie, how many pieces are there?

______

What fraction shows the whole cookie? ______

Name ______________________________

9-5

Homework Practice

2NS4.2, 2MR1.2

Compare Fractions

Chapter Resources

Use < or >.

1. 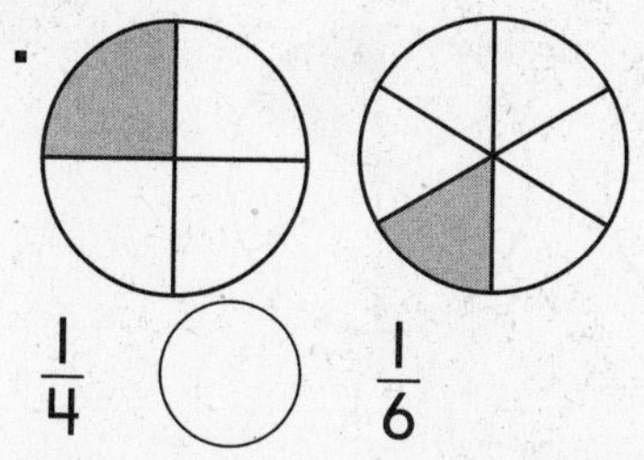

$\frac{1}{4}$ $\frac{1}{6}$

2. 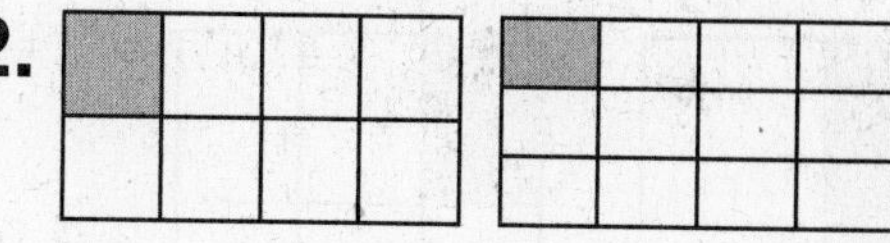

$\frac{1}{8}$ $\frac{1}{12}$

3. 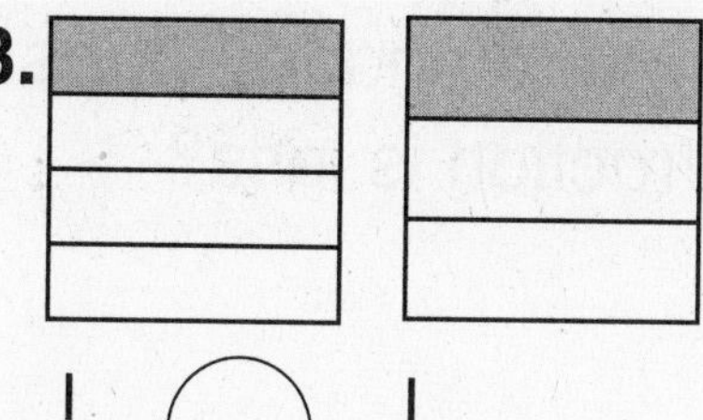

$\frac{1}{4}$ $\frac{1}{3}$

4. 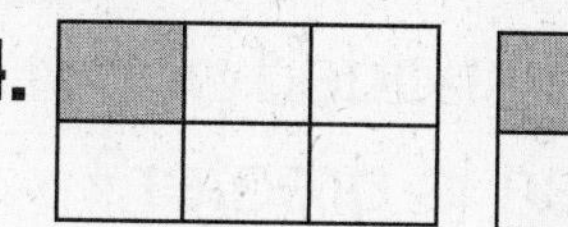

$\frac{1}{6}$ $\frac{1}{8}$

Compare the fractions. Use < or >.

5. $\frac{1}{4}$ 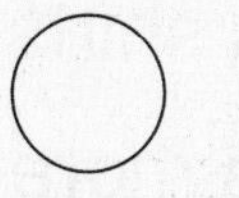 $\frac{1}{2}$

6. $\frac{1}{4}$ 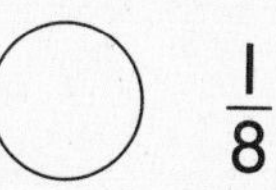 $\frac{1}{8}$

7. $\frac{1}{6}$ 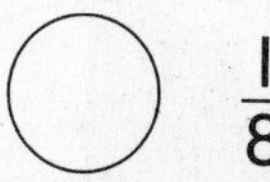 $\frac{1}{8}$

8. $\frac{1}{12}$ 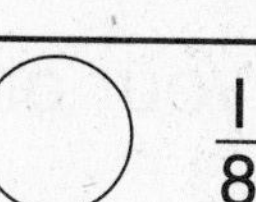 $\frac{1}{8}$

9. $\frac{1}{6}$ 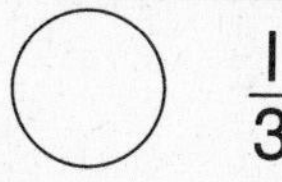 $\frac{1}{3}$

10. $\frac{1}{6}$ 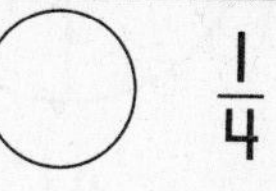 $\frac{1}{4}$

Solve.

11. Lee and Tim are wearing hats. $\frac{1}{4}$ of Lee's hat is red. $\frac{1}{6}$ of Tim's hat is red. Whose hat has more red? Explain.

____

12. Jeff and Fran each have 12 shoes. $\frac{1}{3}$ of Jeff's shoes are black. $\frac{2}{3}$ of Fran's shoes are black. Who has more black shoes? Explain.

____

Name ______________________________

9-5

Problem-Solving Practice

2NS4.2, 2MR1.2

Compare Fractions

Solve.

1. 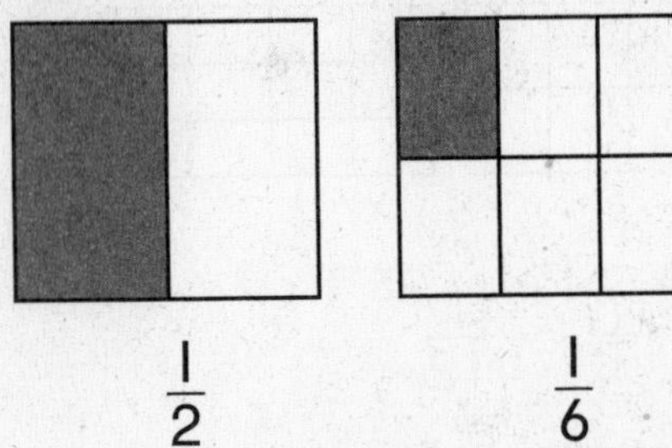

$\frac{1}{2}$ $\frac{1}{6}$

Compare the shaded parts.
Which fraction is greater?

______

2. 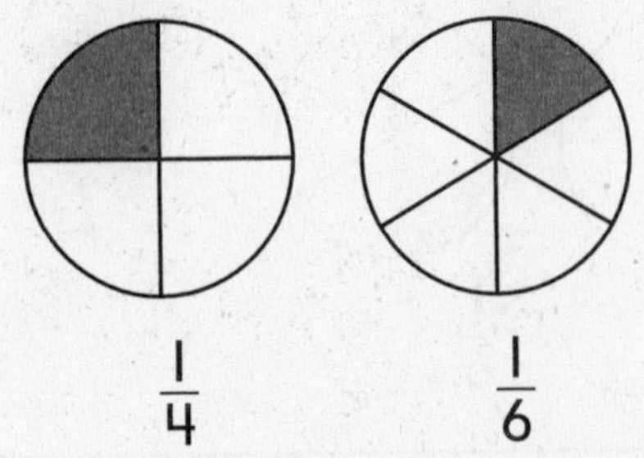

$\frac{1}{4}$ $\frac{1}{6}$

Compare the shaded parts.
Which fraction is less?

______

3. Al eats $\frac{1}{4}$ of a cookie. Ling eats $\frac{1}{3}$ of a cookie.

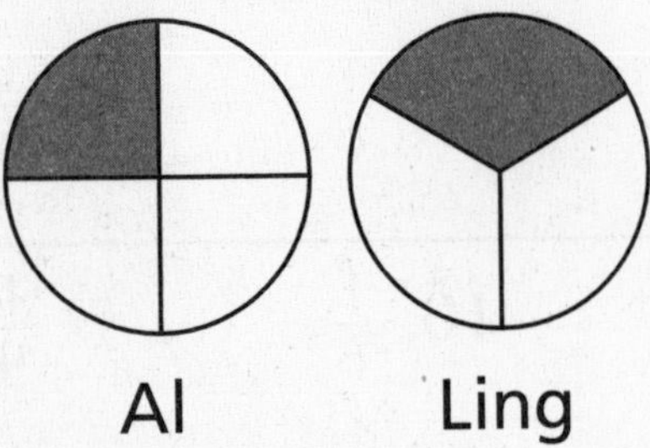

Who eats more? ______

4. Ellen and Gil each have 8 shirts. $\frac{1}{2}$ of Ellen's shirts are white. $\frac{1}{4}$ of Gil's shirts are white. Who has more white shirts? Prove your answer.

____

____

5. Tom and Greg each order a sandwich. Tom eats $\frac{1}{2}$ of his sandwich. Greg eats $\frac{1}{3}$ of his sandwich. Who eats more? Explain.

____

6. There are 6 fish in a tank. $\frac{2}{6}$ of the fish are orange. There are 6 fish in a bowl. $\frac{3}{6}$ of the fish are orange. Does the tank or the bowl have more orange fish?

____

Name ______________________________

9-6

Homework Practice

2NS4.2, 2MR1.2

Unit Fractions of a Group

Chapter Resources

Write the fraction for the shaded parts.

1. 

______

2. 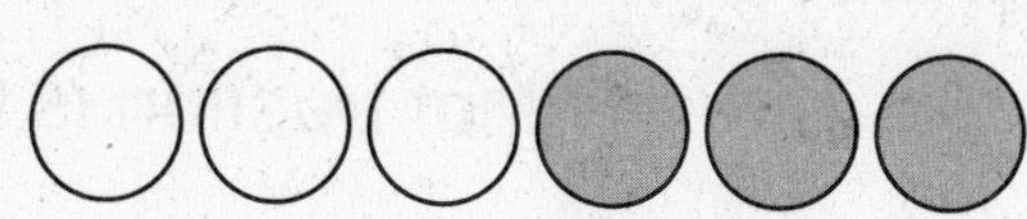

______

3. 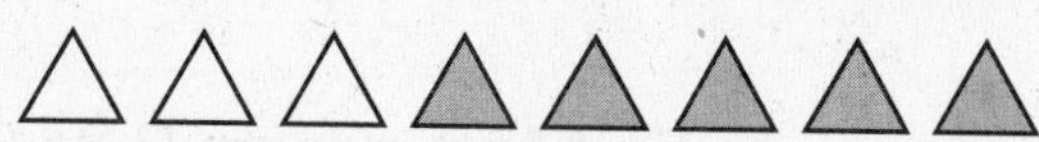

______

Write the fraction. Use the picture to solve.

4. Farmer Bean buys 6 new animals for his farm. What fraction of the animals are sheep?

______

5. Liza feeds these 4 animals at the park today. What fraction of the animals are rabbits?

______

Solve.

6. 9 + 9 + 7 = ______

7. 6 + 8 + 4 = ______

8. 5 + 8 + 5 = ______

9. 7 + 8 + 3 = ______

Name ______________________________

9-6

Problem-Solving Practice

2NS4.2, 2MR1.2

Fractions of a Group

For 1–3, circle the correct answer. For 4–6, solve.

1. 

1 of Cam's counters is black.

What fraction is black?

$\frac{1}{2}$ $\frac{1}{3}$ $\frac{1}{4}$

2. 3 of Jim's counters are black.

What fraction is black?

$\frac{1}{5}$ $\frac{2}{5}$ $\frac{3}{5}$

3. Matt dropped 4 pennies. This picture shows how they landed.

What fraction shows how many pennies landed heads up?

$\frac{1}{4}$ $\frac{2}{4}$ $\frac{3}{4}$

4. Matt drops 2 more pennies.

Now what fraction of the group shows heads?

____

5. Jake has 5 balloons. $\frac{3}{5}$ of Jake's balloons are orange. Shade the number of balloons that are orange.

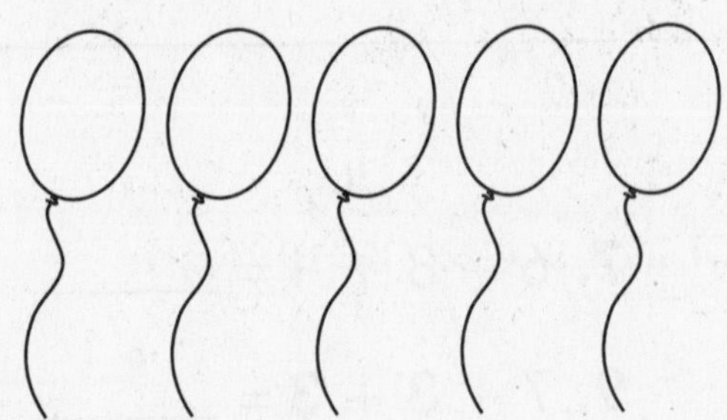

6. 6 birds are in a tree. Half of them fly away. How many birds are still in the tree?

______ birds

Draw a picture to explain.

Name ______________________________

9-7

Homework Practice

2NS4.2

Other Fractions of a Group

Chapter Resources

Preparation: Crayons are needed for this activity.

Color to show the fraction of the group.

1. $\frac{3}{3}$ of the stars are blue.

2. $\frac{5}{6}$ of the hearts are pink.

3. $\frac{3}{8}$ of the circles are red.

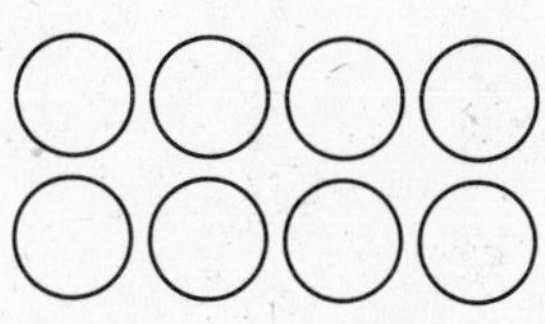

4. $\frac{3}{4}$ of the squares are green.

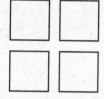

5. $\frac{1}{6}$ of the triangles are yellow.

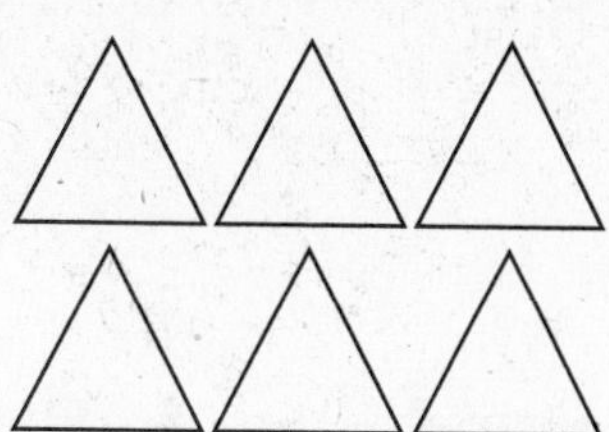

6. $\frac{1}{2}$ of the suns are orange.

Solve.

7. Mrs. Chen buys four pies. Three pies are apple and one is cherry. Use a fraction to write how many of the pies are apple.

______

8. Jan has 8 coins. She has 3 quarters, 3 dimes, and 2 pennies. Use a fraction to write how many of the coins are dimes.

______

Name ___________________________

9-7

Problem-Solving Practice

2NS4.2

Other Fractions of a Group

Circle or write the correct answer.

1. Han has 4 marbles. 1 of the 4 marbles is blue. What fraction of the marbles is blue?

$\frac{1}{4}$ $\frac{3}{4}$ $\frac{4}{4}$

2. Joey has 5 apples. 2 of the 5 apples are red. What fraction of the apples is red?

______

3. What fraction of the fish is striped?

______

4. Ginger gave $\frac{2}{5}$ of her shells to Howard. Shade the number of shells Ginger gave to Howard.

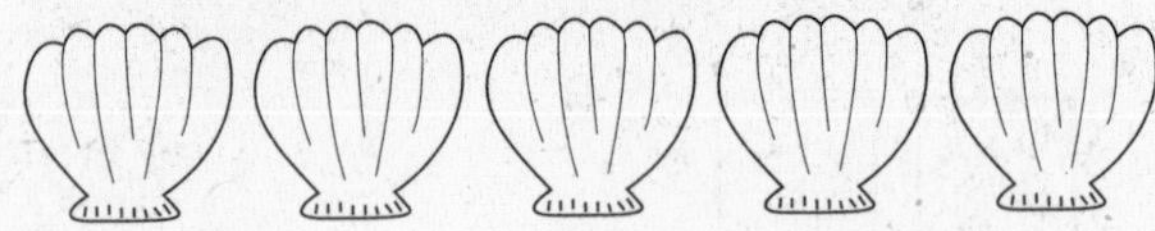

5. Ingrid has 2 green bottles and 3 yellow bottles. How many does she have in all?

______ bottles

What fraction is green?

______

6. Steve has 4 red cars and 2 blue cars. How many cars does he have in all?

______ cars

What fraction is blue?

______

What fraction is red? ______

Name ______________________________

9-8

Homework Practice

2NS4.2, 2MR1.1

Problem-Solving Investigation: Choose a Strategy

Choose a strategy to answer each question.

Problem-Solving Strategies
- Use a Pattern
- Write a Number Sentence
- Make a Table

1. Terry buys a bagel. He cuts it in half. Then he cuts the pieces in half again. How many pieces of bagel does Terry have?

______

2. There are 16 apples in a bag. If each child gets 4 of the apples, how many children are there?

______ children

3. Cory and Josh have six pinwheels. Two pinwheels are orange and the rest are pink. Use a fraction to name the pink pinwheels. If possible, use a strategy you have not already used here. ______

4. Steve has 4 cats on his farm. Each cat has 3 kittens. How many kittens are on Steve's farm?

______ kittens

5. Elena's mom bakes 12 muffins. She keeps 4 muffins for Elena. She gives the other muffins to friends. What fraction shows how many muffins her friends have?

______

Name ______________________________

10-1

Homework Practice

2NS1.0

Hundreds

Chapter Resources

Write how many tens and how many ones. Then write the number.

1. 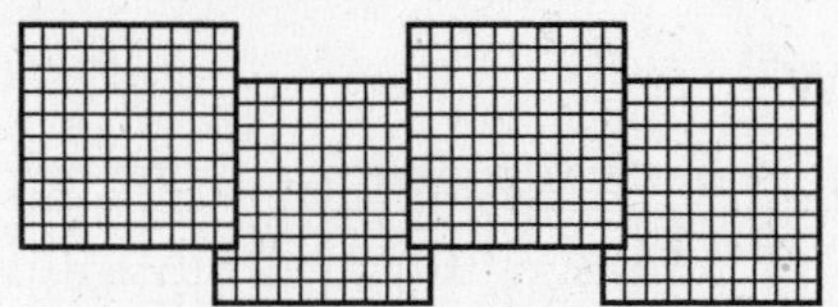

4 hundreds = ______ tens =

______ ones = ______

2. 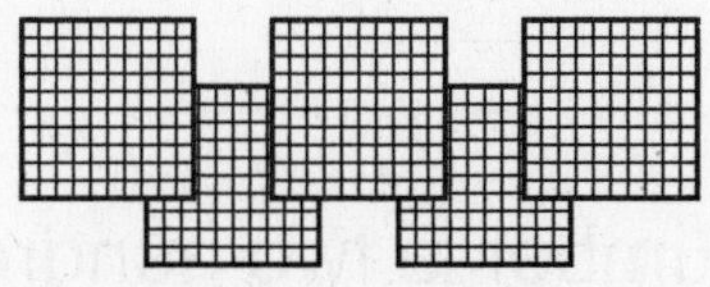

5 hundreds = ______ tens =

______ ones = ______

3. 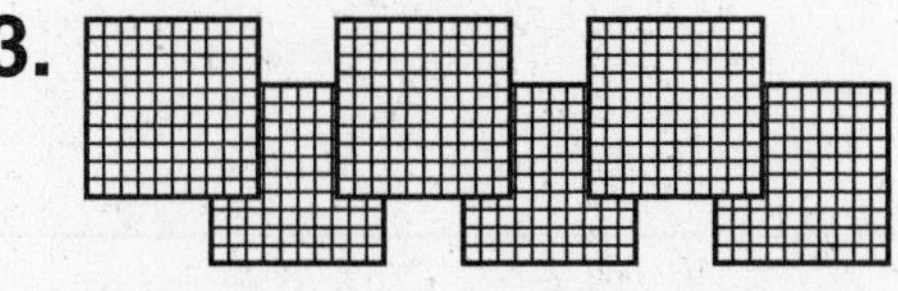

6 hundreds = ______ tens =

______ ones = ______

4. 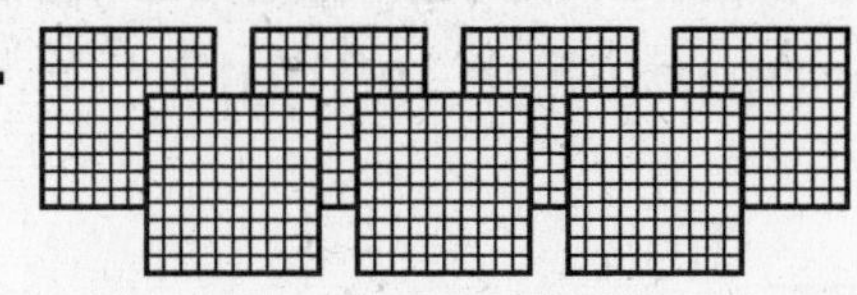

7 hundreds = ______ tens =

______ ones = ______

Solve.

5. Malika has 9 sheets of stickers. 100 stickers are on each sheet. How many stickers does Malika have?

9 hundreds = ______ tens = ______ ones = ______ stickers

6. Circle every answer with an even number in the hundreds place.

Name ____________________

10-1

Problem-Solving Practice

2NS1.0

Hundreds

Solve.

1. What number does this show?

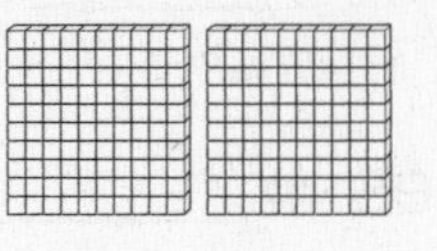

______

2. What number does this show?

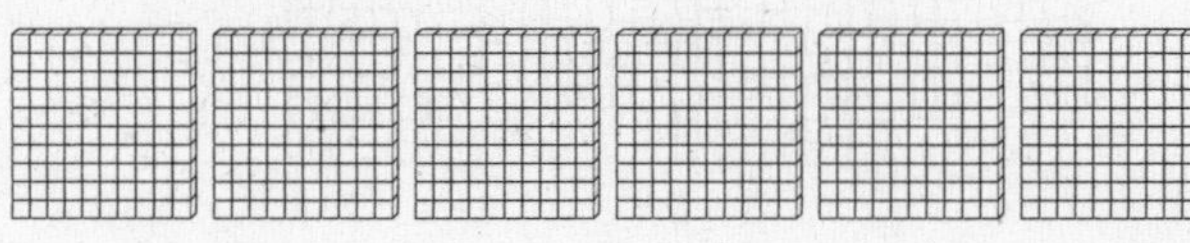

______

3. What number is one hundred less than 500?

______

4. What number is two hundred more than 500?

______

5. How many people are in the park? Raul counted 10 tens. How many people is that?

______ people

6. How many fish are in the pet store? Leah counted 70 tens. How many fish is that?

______ fish

7. Joel has a roll of 50 dimes. He goes to the bank and trades the dimes for dollar bills. How many dollars does he get?

______ dollars

8. Kali has 3 dollars but she needs dimes. She trades the dollars for dimes. How many dimes does she get?

______ dimes

Name ____________________

10-2

Homework Practice

2NS1.1, 2NS1.2

Hundreds, Tens, and Ones

Chapter Resources

Write how many hundreds, tens, and ones.

1. 165

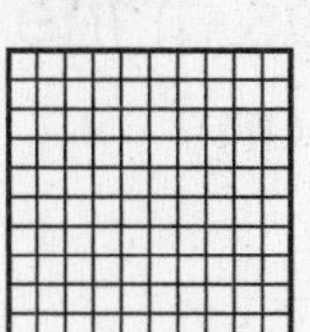

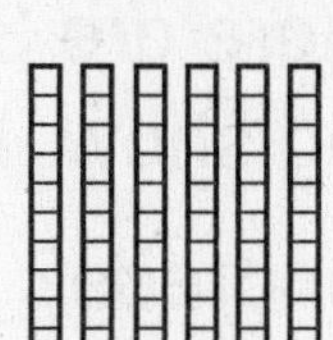

hundreds	tens	ones

____ hundred ____ tens ____ ones

2. 328

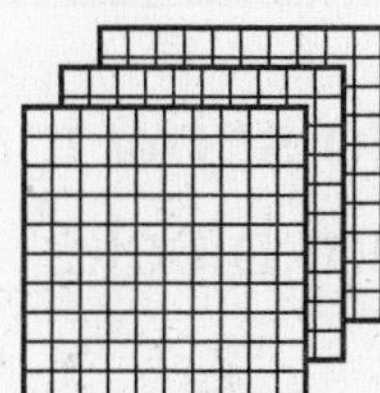

hundreds	tens	ones

____ hundreds ____ tens ____ ones

3. 671

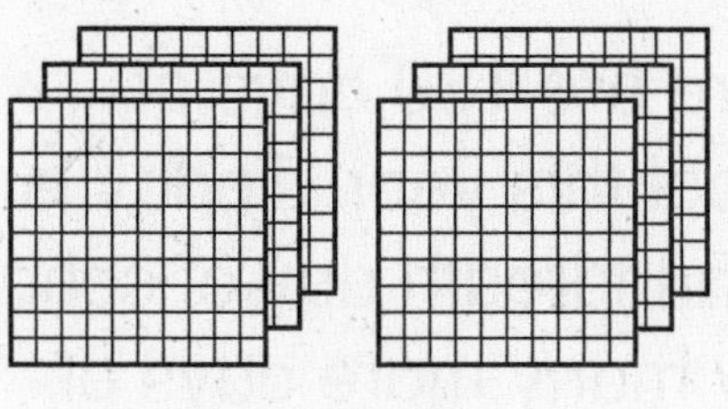

hundreds	tens	ones

____ hundreds ____ tens ____ one

Solve.

4. Cal sees 416 geese at the park. How many ones? _______ ones
How many hundreds? _______ hundreds

5. Find the pattern. Write the missing number.
10, 20, 30, _______, 50, _______, _______

Name ____________________

10-2

Problem-Solving Practice

2NS1.1, 2NS1.2

Hundreds, Tens, and Ones

Solve.

1. The bagel shop makes 576 bagels. How many hundreds? ________

How many tens? ________

How many ones? ________

2. There are 390 dogs at the dog show. How many hundreds? ________

How many tens? ________

How many ones? ________

3. Val uses blocks to show the number 283. What blocks does she use?

________ hundreds

________ tens ________ ones

4. Bill uses blocks to show the number 148. What blocks does he use?

________ hundred

________ tens ________ ones

5. Pete brings 24 crayons to school. His teacher has a box of 100 crayons. If they put the crayons together, what number will they show?

________ crayons

6. There are 180 days of school this year. Today is the hundredth day of school. How many more days of school are there this year?

________ more days

7. You have 4 hundreds 7 tens and 3 ones. What number do you have?

____

8. You have 6 tens 9 ones and 5 hundreds. What number do you have?

____

Name ______________________________

10-3

Homework Practice

2MR2.2, 2SDAP1.1

Problem-Solving Strategy: Make a List

Preparation: A separate piece of paper is needed for this activity.

Make a list to solve. Use a separate piece of paper.

1. Tim is spelling his name with alphabet magnets. How many ways can he combine his name letters?

   Tim's letters can be combined in ______ ways.

2. Lin needs to make a sign. She can choose large, medium, or small for the size. She can choose red, yellow, or blue for the color. How many different signs can Lin make?

   Lin can make ______ different signs.

3. Pablo has 3 boxes. The boxes are marked 7, 8, and 9. How many ways can Pablo stack the boxes?

   Pablo can stack boxes ______ ways.

4. Kiki is making party favors. She can give a marker set or puzzle set. She can put them in a silver bag or a gold bag. How many different kinds of party favors can Kiki make?

   Kiki can make ______ kinds of party favors.

5. Emily cannot remember her house number. She knows it has the numbers 5, 2, and 9. How many different three-digit numbers could it be? Write them.

   ____

Name ____________________

10-4

Homework Practice

2NS1.1, 2NS1.2

Place Value to 1,000

Chapter Resources

Write each number in expanded form.

1. 253

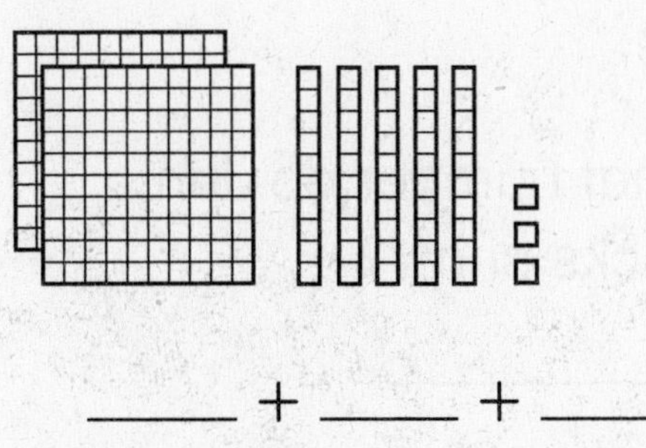

_____ + _____ + _____

2. 418

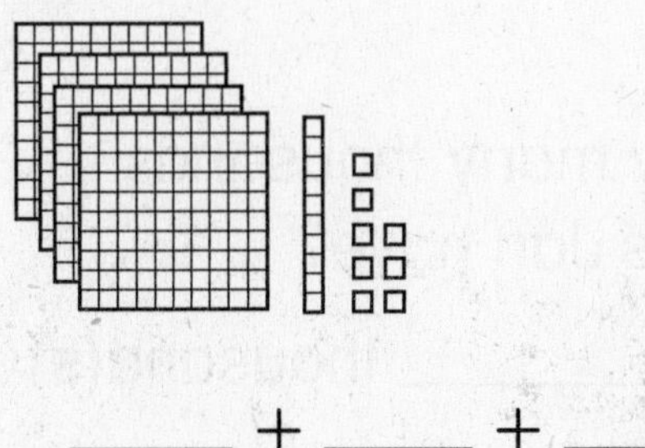

_____ + _____ + _____

3. 1,000

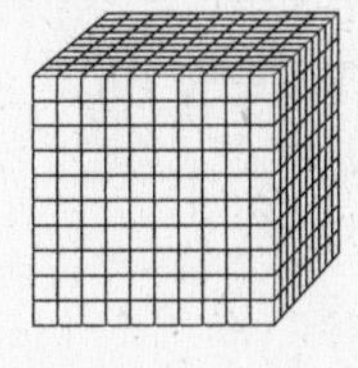

_____ + _____ + _____ + _____

4. 547

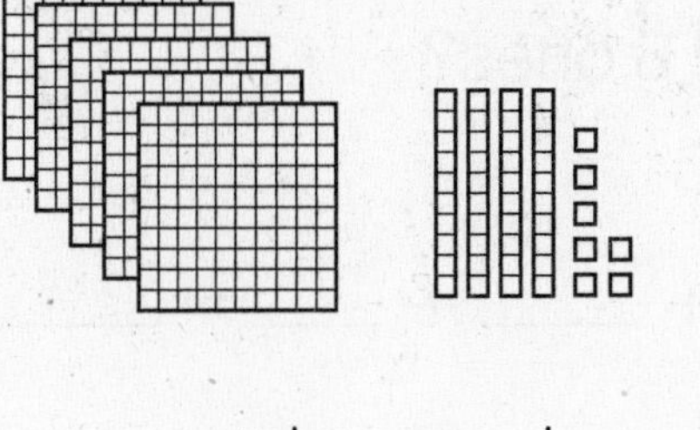

_____ + _____ + _____

Solve.

5. Trey reads that 1,483 people went to the baseball game. How can Trey show how many people in expanded form?

_____ + _____ + _____ + _____ = 1,483 people

6. Sofia's school sells 310 raffle tickets. She is writing the number of tickets in expanded form.

How many ones will she write? _____ ones

Name ____________________

10-4

Problem-Solving Practice

2NS1.1, 2NS1.2

Place Value to 1,000

Solve.

Jan's Blocks

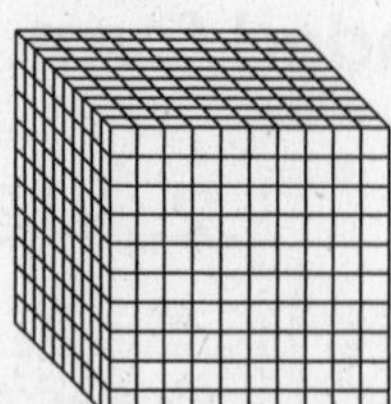

1. How many thousands does Jan have?

   ________ thousand(s)

2. What number do Jan's blocks show?

   ____

3. How can Mira write 4 hundreds, 3 tens, and 8 ones?

   ____ + ____ + ____ = ______

4. Juan's pen pal lives 816 miles away. How can Juan write how many miles in expanded form?

   ____ + ____ + ____

   = _____ miles

5. Mario wanted to write the number 901. He wrote 900 + 10 + 1. Is this right? If not, make it right.

   ____ + ____ + ____

   = _____

6. Bess counted all the crayons in her house. There were 143. Write how many crayons in expanded form.

   _____ + _____ + _____

   = 143 crayons

Name ______________________________

10-5

Homework Practice

2NS1.1, 2NS1.2

Read and Write Numbers to 1,000

Chapter Resources

Circle the correct number word.

1. 813
eight hundred thirteen
eight hundred thirty

2. 501
five hundred one
five hundred ten

Read the number. Write it in 2 different ways.

4.

hundreds	tens	ones
7	1	2

____

_____ + _____ + _____ = _____

5. six hundred eighty-three

hundreds	tens	ones

_____ + _____ + _____ = _____

Solve.

7. Rani knows that there are three hundred sixty-five days in one year. How can Rani use expanded notation to show this number?

_____ + _____ + _____ = _____ days

8. Aaron uses this chart to show how many marbles he has. How can he write the number in words?

hundreds	tens	ones
1	5	2

______________________________ marbles

10-5

Name ______________________________

Problem-Solving Practice

2NS1.1, 2NS1.2

Read and Write Numbers to 1,000

Solve.

1. Ms. Kim has 322 CDs. Use expanded form to write how many.

   _______ + ______ + ______ = _______ CDs

2. Sari's school is making 1,000 paper cranes. Circle the number word that shows how many.
   one hundred
   one thousand

3. Diego's Diner has been open 190 days. Use words to write how many days. ______________________________

4. The Valley Vet Office has helped 823 sick pets. How can the vet use a place-value chart to show this number?

hundreds	tens	ones

5. Dwayne heard that there are four hundred thirty-nine fish at the zoo. Dwayne used a place-value chart to show the number. How many tens in his chart? ______ tens

6. The town sports arena has 952 seats. Mira wrote how many seats in expanded form. Is she correct? If not, fix her numbers.
   900 + 52 = 952 seats.

   ______ + ______ + ______ = _______ seats

Name ______________________________

10-6

Homework Practice

2NS2.0, 2MR1.1

Problem-Solving Investigation: Choose a Strategy

Chapter Resources

Preparation: Access to hundred, base-ten, and unit cubes is needed for this activity.

Solve.

Problem-Solving Strategies
Make an organized list
Write a number sentence
Use a model

1. Jay has more than 348 buttons. He has less than 501 buttons. The number of buttons has a 5 in the hundreds place. Write the number word that shows how many buttons.

______________________ buttons

2. Velma has 721 blocks. She wants to group her blocks into hundreds, tens, and ones. How many tens does Velma have?

_____ tens

3. Ben has five hundred shells. He finds twelve more on the beach. How many shells does Ben have now?

_____ shells

4. Mr. Sun is thinking of a number. It is less than 398. It is more than 387. Mr. Sun's number has a 5 in the ones place. What is Mr. Sun's number?

_____

Name ______________________________

10-7

Homework Practice

2NS1.3

Compare Numbers

Compare. Write >, <, or =.

1. 415 ◯ 451	623 ◯ 678	730 ◯ 830
2. 375 ◯ 375	549 ◯ 560	248 ◯ 239
3. 109 ◯ 111	382 ◯ 379	445 ◯ 545
4. 272 ◯ 275	818 ◯ 816	357 ◯ 357
5. 643 ◯ 637	256 ◯ 261	429 ◯ 421
6. 317 ◯ 371	588 ◯ 598	761 ◯ 769

Solve.

7. The number of buttons in Jill's jar is greater than 6 hundreds 3 tens and 7 ones. The number of buttons in Jill's jar is less than 6 hundreds 3 tens 9 ones. How many buttons are in Jill's jar?

______ buttons

8. Circle the correct answer.
Uri has 529 bugs in his collection. Elena has 513 bugs in her collection.
529 is ____________ 513 **greater than** **less than** **equal to**

Who has a greater number of bugs? ______

9. Look back over the page. Circle every number with a 5 in the tens place.

Name ___

10-7

Problem-Solving Practice

2NS1.3

Compare Numbers

Solve. Write < or >, if needed.

1. 475 people go to the circus. 529 people go to the fair. More people go to the ___.

2. Faye bakes 255 muffins. Cesar bakes 235 muffins.
___ bakes a greater number of muffins.

3. Benji has 223 marbles. Steve has 530 marbles.
223 ◯ 530
Who has the greater number of marbles?
___

4. Don has 712 corn stalks. He has 312 tomato plants.
712 ◯ 312
Does he have more corn stalks or tomato plants?
___

5. Seth saves 347 bottle caps. Jorge saves 345. Who saves the greater number of bottle caps?
___

6. Ms. Chavez can buy an airplane ticket on sale for $299. The regular price of the ticket is $100 more. Is the regular price greater than or less than $400?
___
Explain. ___
___
___

Name ______________________________

10-8

Homework Practice

2NS1.3

Order Numbers

Chapter Resources

Order the numbers from *least* to *greatest*.

1. 274, 248, 312, 291 ______, ______, ______, ______

2. 682, 628, 631, 619 ______, ______, ______, ______

3. 485, 554, 444, 452 ______, ______, ______, ______

Order the numbers from *greatest* to *least*.

4. 387, 235, 412, 370 ______, ______, ______, ______

5. 919, 901, 991, 109 ______, ______, ______, ______

6. 832, 328, 283, 823 ______, ______, ______, ______

7. 717, 117, 171, 771 ______, ______, ______, ______

Solve.

8. The Old Hen Theater sold 749 tickets on Friday, 984 tickets on Saturday, and 621 tickets on Sunday. How can you order ticket sales from *least* to *greatest*?

______, ______, ______

9. On Monday, The Old Hen Theater sold 670 tickets. How can you order the new ticket sales from *greatest* to *least*?

______, ______, ______, ______

Name ______________________________

10-8

Problem-Solving Practice

2NS1.3

Order Numbers

Solve.

1. Melba writes down how many people come to the fair each day: 346, 124, 518. Order the numbers from *least* to *greatest*.

   ______, ______, ______

2. Gina has 659 coins. Paco has 584 coins. Orin has 725 coins. Order the numbers of coins from *greatest* to *least*.

   ______, ______, ______

   Who has the least coins?

   ______

3. Some classrooms at school have these numbers: Class 207, Class 211, Class 243, and Class 208. Order them from *least* to *greatest*.

   ______, ______, ______, ______

4. The students are playing a number game. Tess picks 483. Jamie picks 492 and Sadie picks 439. Jenny picks 432. Order the numbers from *greatest* to *least*.

   ______, ______, ______, ______

5. The school collects cans for recycling. Grade 2 recycles 607 cans. Grade 3 recycles 289 cans. Grade 4 recycles 812 cans.

   __________ recycles the least amount of cans.

6. Holly has 490 animal stickers, 173 sports stickers, and 723 space stickers. Holly has the greatest

   amount of __________

   stickers.

Name ____________________

Homework Practice

2SDAP2.0

Number Patterns

Write the missing numbers. Then write the pattern.

1. 1000, 999, _____, 997, _____

   Each number is ____________.

2. 524, _____, 544, 554, _____

   Each number is ____________.

3. _____, 283, 383, _____, 583

   Each number is ____________.

4. _____, 843, 743, 643, _____

   Each number is ____________.

5. 953, 943, _____, 923, _____

   Each number is ____________.

Use the pattern to solve.

6. Tarik's computer prints this number pattern: 535, 525, 515, 505, 495.
   What should the next number be? _____

7. Ellie's Deli is recording the number of sandwiches sold each month for 5 months: 723, 733, 743, 753, 763.
   If sandwich sales continue this pattern, how many will sell next month?

   _____ sandwiches

10-9

Name ______________________________

Problem-Solving Practice

2SDAP2.0

Number Patterns

Solve.

1. Jody is counting out loud: 511, 512, 513, 514, 515, 516. What counting pattern is Jody using?

   Each number is __________.

2. Phil writes these numbers in his notebook:

   236, 246, ______, 266,

   ______, 286. Write the missing numbers. Name the pattern.

   Each number is __________.

3. Paul counts by hundreds. He starts with the number 123. Write the numbers Paul counts.

   123, ______, ______, ______,

   ______, ______

4. Alli counts by tens. She starts with the number 325. Write the numbers Alli counts.

   325, ______, ______, ______,

   ______, ______

5. Shari and Miguel play a game. Shari counts: 169, 159, 149, 139, 129. Shari wants Miguel to guess her counting pattern. What should Miguel guess?

   Each number is __________.

6. It is Miguel's turn to play. He counts: 125, 140, 130, 135, 120, 145. Put Miguel's numbers in order from *greatest* to *least*.

   ______, ______, ______,

   ______, ______, ______

   Guess the counting pattern.

   Each number is __________.

Name ___________________________________

11-1

Homework Practice

2MG2.0

Solid Shapes

Sphere

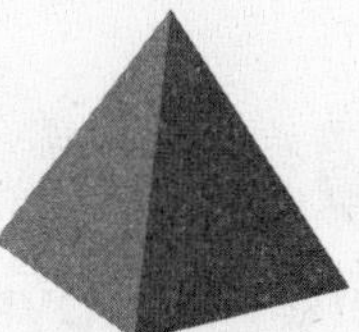
Pyramid

Square

Rectangular prism

Cone

Cylinder

Write the name of the solid shapes that are the same. Circle the one that is different.

1.  ______________________

2.  ______________________

3.  ______________________

4.  ______________________

Solve.

5.   Hank has something in the shape of a cone. Find and circle it.

6.  Rover has something shaped like a sphere. Find and circle it.

Name ______________________________

11-1

Problem-Solving Practice

2MG2.0

Solid Shapes

rectangular prism

cone

cylinder

sphere

pyramid

Write the answer.

1. Which figure is the same shape as Tim's math book?

____

2. Dawn wants to roll a shape. Which shape can she roll?

____

3. Taylor is at the ball field. He sees an object in the shape of a sphere. Is it a soccer ball or a football?

____

4. David is at a party. Ms. White gives him an object shaped like a cylinder. Is it a party hat or a glass of punch?

____

5. Brent has a cylinder. He can put flowers in it. Is Brent's cylinder a vase or a sink?

____

6. Maria has a rectangular prism. One of the sides has an opening. She needs this when she sneezes. What is Maria's rectangular prism?

____

Name ______________________________

11-2

Homework Practice

2MG2.1, 2MR1.2

Faces, Edges, and Vertices

Circle the figures that match the description.

1. 6 faces, 12 edges, 8 vertices

2. 0 faces, 0 edges, 0 vertices

3. 1 face, 0 edges, 1 vertex

4. 2 faces, 0 edges, 0 vertices

Solve.

5. Nate's shoes come in a box that has 6 faces, 12 edges, and 8 vertices. What shape is Nate's shoe box?

____

6. Anne builds a shape that has 5 faces, 8 edges, and 5 vertices.

What shape does Anne build? ______________________

Chapter Resources

Name ______________________

11-2

Problem-Solving Practice

2MG2.1, 2MR1.2

Faces, Edges, and Vertices

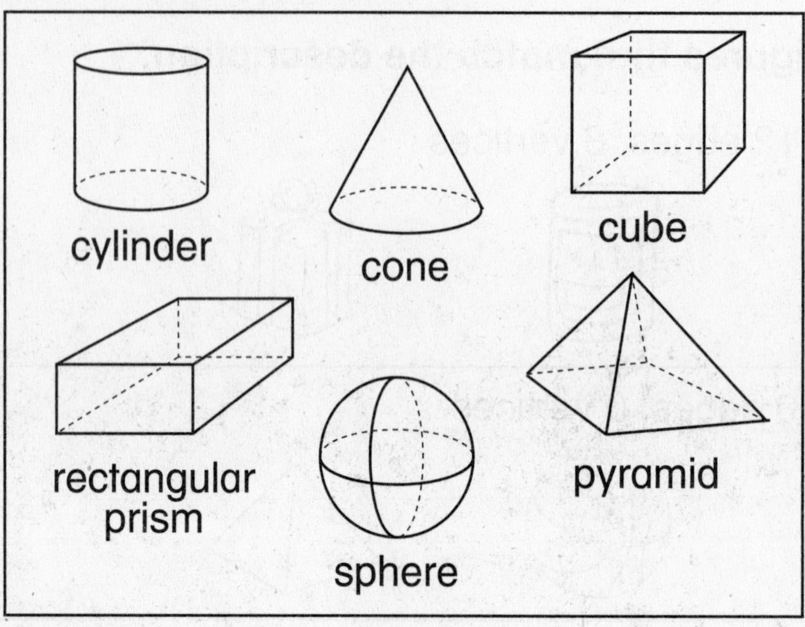

Write the answer.

1. Lucy draws a shape with 2 faces. What shape does Lucy draw?

   ____

2. Ben draws a shape with 1 face. What shape does Ben draw?

   ____

3. Ned is playing with a figure that has no faces. What is the shape?

   ____

4. Tina's juice comes in a shape with no vertices. What is the shape?

   ____

5. Lin is making a sandwich. She opens an object in the shape of a cylinder. Is it bread or peanut butter?

   ____

6. Jon is thinking about something in his yard. It is shaped like a cone. Is it a pine tree or a bush?

   ____

11-3

Name ______________________________

Homework Practice

2MG2.0

Plane Shapes

Chapter Resources

Connect the dots to make the shape. Name the shape.

1. ____________________

2. ____________________

3. ____________________

4. ____________________

Write the answer.

5. 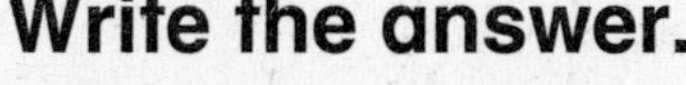

Ray drew this picture. How many of each did he draw?

_____ rectangles _____ circles

6. 

Tony made a picture using different shapes. How many of each did he draw? _____ rectangles _____ triangles

Name ______________________________

11-3

Problem-Solving Practice

2MG2.0

Plane Shapes

Write the answer.

1.   Circle the **parallelograms**.

2. 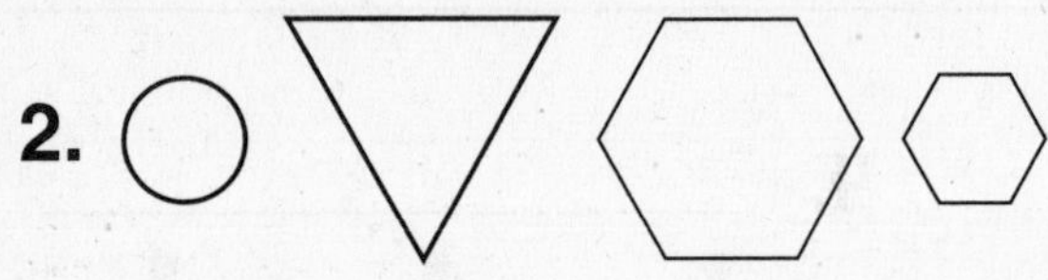 Circle the **hexagons**.

3. What shape is this sign? 

____

4. What shape is this honeycomb? 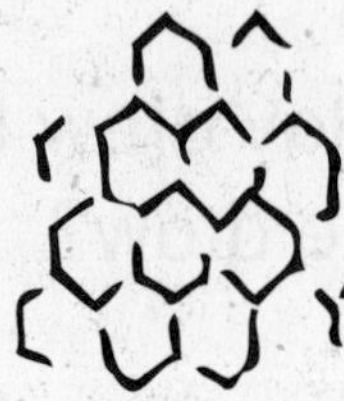 ______________

5. 

What shape is this coin?

____

6. How many rectangles do you see in this picture?

______ rectangles ______ triangle

Name ______________________________

11-4

Homework Practice

2MR1.0, 2SDAP2.1

Problem-Solving Strategy: Find a Pattern

Find a pattern to solve. Write your answer.

1. Beth saw this pattern in a book. What three shapes come next?

_______ _______ _______

2. Leo sees this pattern on a poster.

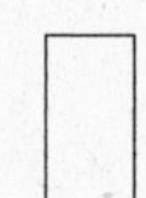
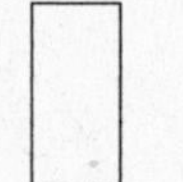
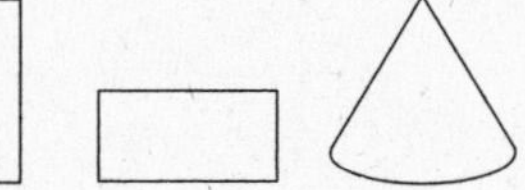

What three shapes come next?

_______ _______ _______

3. Mark says he sees a pattern on a building. He sees

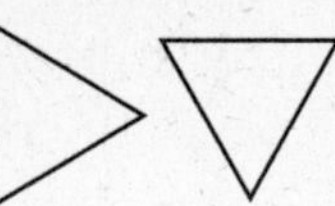

Is he right? __________

4. One dog has four legs.
Two dogs have eight legs.
How many legs do six dogs have? ______ legs

5. Deb painted 3 flowers in the first row.
She painted 6 flowers in the second row, and 9 flowers in the third row. How many flowers would be in the eight row, if the pattern continues? ______ flowers

Name ____________________

11-5

Homework Practice

2MG2.0, 2MG2.1

Sides and Vertices

Chapter Resources

Connect the shape to its number of sides or vertices.

1. hexagon	4 sides
2. parallelogram	no vertices
3. triangle	6 vertices
4. circle	3 sides

Write the name of the shape. Tell two things about it.

5. 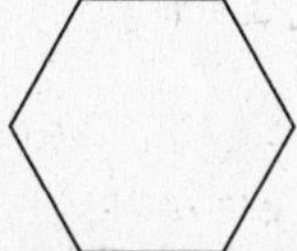

6. 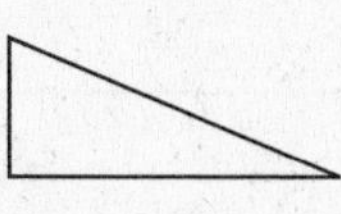

7. 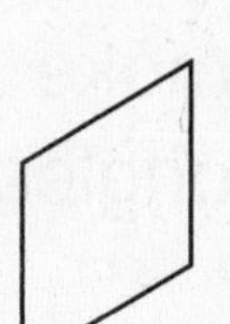

Name ____________________

11-5

Problem-Solving Practice

2MG2.0, 2MG2.1

Sides and Vertices

circle

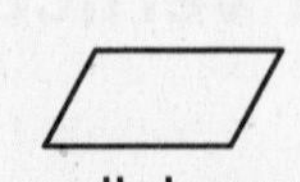
parallelogram

rectangle

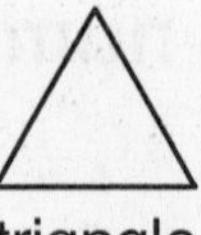
triangle

square

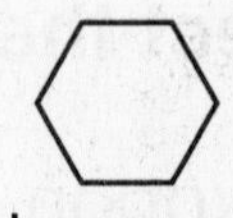
hexagon

Write the answer.

1. Kira draws a plane shape with 6 sides. What shape does she draw?

____

2. Alex draws a plane shape with 3 angles. What shape does Alex draw?

____

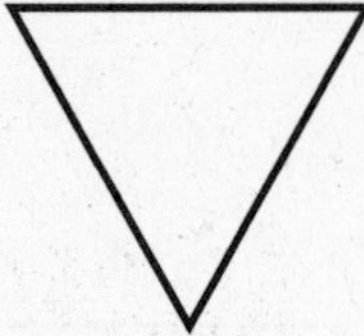

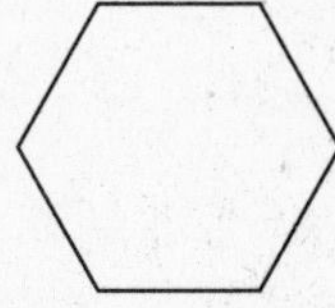

3. What shapes are in the picture?

____

____

____

4. If triangle had 1 more side, what shape would it be?

____

5. Kay can draw 3 different shapes with 4 vertices. What are they?

____

____

____

6. Bill draws 1 line to make a shape. It has no angles. What is the shape?

____

Name ______________________________

11-6

Homework Practice

2MG2.0, 2MR1.2

Relate Plane Shapes to Solid Shapes

Chapter Resources

Look at the solid shape. Draw the plane shape you would make if you traced it.

1. 

2. 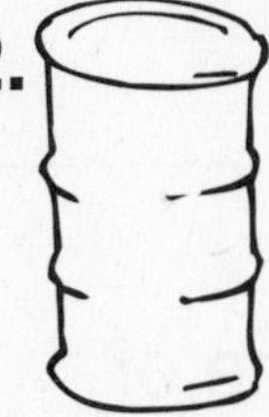

3. 

4. 

Solve.

5. Jerry drew a shape with one circle face. The shape has one vertex. What shape did he draw? ______________________

6. Mary traced the face of a can. What shape did she make?

____

7. What shape has zero vertices and zero sides?

____

Name ____________________

11-6

Problem-Solving Practice

2MG2.0, 2MR1.2

Relate Plane Shapes to Solid Shapes

For 1 and 2, draw the shape.
For 3–6, write the answer.

1. Jen has a number cube. What shape can she trace from her cube?

____

2. Aaron has an ice-cream cone. What shape can he trace from his cone?

____

3. Nat traces the face of a cylinder. What shape does he make?

____

4. Grace traces the face of a rectangular prism. What shape does she make?

____

5. Emily is drawing a square. She traces the face of a solid shape to make one. What does she use?

____

6. Zack is drawing a circle. He traces the face of a solid shape to make one. What figure does he use?

____

7. Seth has a pyramid. What two shapes could he trace with this piece?

____

8. Compare a triangle and a pyramid. How are they alike?

____

____

____

Name ______________________________

11-7

Homework Practice

2MG2.2, 2MR1.2

Make New Shapes

Chapter Resources

Preparation: Pattern blocks are needed for this activity.

Use triangles and squares to make new shapes.

1. Make a rectangle.

____

2. Make a square.

____

3. Make a parallelogram.

____

4. Make a trapezoid.

____

Write the answer. Use blocks to help.

5. Anna wants to make a trapezoid. How many triangles will she need?______ triangles

6. Mike has a some triangles. How many will he need to make a hexagon? ______ triangles

11-7

Name ______________________________

Problem-Solving Practice

2MG2.2, 2MR1.2

Make New Shapes

Preparation: Pattern blocks are needed for this activity.

Write the answer. Use pattern blocks to help.

1. Anton puts 2 triangles together. What shape does he make?

   ____

2. Emma puts 2 squares together. What shape does she make?

   ____

3. Nick makes a hexagon with 2 pattern blocks of the same shape. What shape does he use?

   ____

4. Sue makes a trapezoid with 3 pattern blocks of the same shape. What shape does she use?

   ____

5. Frank uses 4 shapes to make a hexagon. Some of the shapes are alike. Some are different. What shapes does he use?

   ____

   ____

   Draw the hexagon.

6. Ann says she knows 2 different ways to make a hexagon with pattern block shapes. What blocks can she use?

   ____

   ____

   ____

   Draw the other way to make a hexagon.

Name ______________________________

11-8

Homework Practice

2MG2.0, 2MR2.2

Problem-Solving Investigation: Choose a Strategy

Choose a strategy to solve.

Problem-Solving Strategies
- Draw a Picture
- Act It Out
- Guess and Check

1. Matt wants to make a rectangle out of smaller shapes. He says he can do it with a square and 2 triangles. Is he right?

   ______

2. Tim says he knows 2 different ways to make a trapezoid with pattern blocks. What blocks can he use?

   ____

3. Carl wants to draw a truck using plane shapes. What shapes he could use?

   ____

4. Two numbers have a product of 20 and a sum of 9. What are the numbers?

   ______ and ______

5. I have 8 edges. I also have 5 faces and 5 vertices. What shape am I?

   ____

Name ______________________________

12-1

Homework Practice

2NS6.1, 2MG1.1

Nonstandard Units

Preparation: Paper clips are needed for this activity.

Find the object. Estimate. Then use [paper clip] to measure.

1. 

Estimate: about ______ [paper clip] Measure: about ______ [paper clip]

2. 

Estimate: about ______ [paper clip] Measure: about ______ [paper clip]

3. 

Estimate: about ______ [paper clip] Measure: about ______ [paper clip]

4. A ribbon is 30 [cube] long. Minny cuts off a piece of ribbon about 10 [cube] long. Write a number sentence to find how much ribbon is left.

______ ◯ ______ ◯ ______ about ______ [cube] left

Chapter Resources

Name ____________________

12-1

Problem-Solving Practice

2NS6.1, 2MG1.1

Nonstandard Units

Solve.

1. A pencil is about 7 long. A pen is about 9 long. About how much longer is the pen?

   ______ – ______ = ______

   The pen is about ______ longer.

2. A crayon is about 6 long. A paper clip is about 3 long. About how much shorter is the paper clip?

   ______ – ______ = ______

   The paper clip is about ______ shorter.

3. Kat's red string is about 12 long. Her blue string is about 8 long. How do the lengths compare? The blue string is

   about ______ shorter.

4. Fred's white straw is about 13 tall. His green straw is about 16 tall. About how much taller is Fred's green straw? The green straw is

   about ______ taller.

5.

Paper Chain Contest	
Room	Length of Paper Chain
A	
B	
C	

Which room has the longest paper chain? ______

6. A fork is 8 long. A spoon is 6 long. A napkin is 9 long. Write three number sentences that compare the lengths of the napkin, fork, and spoon.

   ____

   ____

Name ______________________________

12-2

Homework Practice

2MG1.3, 2NS6.1

Measure to the Nearest Inch

Chapter Resources

Find the object. Estimate.
Then use an inch ruler to measure.

Find	Estimate	Measure
1. math workbook	about ______ inches	______ inches
2. shoe	about ______ inches	______ inches
3. marker	about ______ inches	______ inches

Solve.

4. Six turtles sit in a row. Each turtle is 2 inches wide. About how long is the row of turtles?

   The row is about ______ inches long.

5. Five beetles walk in a line. Each beetle is 3 inches long. About how long is the line of beetles?

   The line is about ______ inches long.

Name ______________________________

12-2

Problem-Solving Practice

2MG1.3, 2MR1.2

Measure to the Nearest Inch

Solve.

1. Tom's book is 12 inches long. Nell's birthday card is 7 inches long. How much shorter is the card than the book?

   ______ – ______ = ______ ______ inches shorter

2. Ira measures a flower and a leaf. The flower is 8 inches tall. The leaf is 3 inches tall. How much taller is the flower than the leaf?

   ______ – ______ ◯ ______ ______ inches longer

3. Ken's pencil box is 10 inches long. His pencils are 7 inches long. How much longer is the pencil box than the pencils?

   ______ inches longer

4. Stan's toy train car is 3 inches long. He adds a car. How long is a train of 2 toy train cars?

   ______ inches

5. Paper clips are 2 inches long. Kelly makes a paper clip chain 8 inches long. How many clips does Kelly have?

   ______ paper clips

6. Tony wants to frame a photo. The photo is 5 inches wide and 7 inches tall. He wants the frame to add 2 inches to each side. How big will the frame be?

   ______ inches wide and

   ______ inches tall

Name ______________________________

12-3

Homework Practice

2MG1.0, 2MR2.2

Inch, Foot, Yard

Chapter Resources

Preparation: An inch ruler and yardstick are needed for this activity.

Find the object. Use inches, feet, or yards.
Estimate. Measure each object in the unit shown.

Find the Object	Estimate	Measure
1.	______ inch(es)	______ inch(es)
2. READ!	______ feet	______ feet
3.	______ yard	______ yard

Solve.

4. Name three things in your classroom that are longer than 1 foot but shorter than 3 feet. Use a yardstick to measure.

____

____

5. Name three things in your classroom that are longer than 3 feet. Use a yardstick to measure.

____

____

Name ______________________________

12-3

Problem-Solving Practice

2MG1.0, 2MR2.2

Inch, Foot, Yard

Solve.

1 foot = 12 inches
1 yard = 3 feet

1. Anna's dad gave her a teddy bear. It is three feet tall. How many inches tall is the bear?

   ______ inches

2. Ms. Li's classroom has a board that is 3 yards long. How long is the board?

   ______ feet

3. Mr. Ryan's class planted a tree. The tree is now 12 feet tall. How many yards tall is the tree?

   The tree is ______ yards tall.

4. The school's wheelchair ramp is 24 feet long. How many yards long is the ramp?

   The ramp is ______ yards long.

5. Jake draws a line that is 2 yards long. Ted draws a line that is 5 feet long. Who drew the longer line? How much longer is it?

   ____________ drew the longer line.
   It is ____________________ longer.

6. Phil is wrapping a gift. The wrapping paper is 2 feet wide and 4 yards long. He cuts a piece that is 2 feet wide and 5 feet long. How wide and long is the piece he has left?

   The leftover paper is ______ feet wide and ______ feet long.

Name ____________________

12-4

Homework Practice

2MG1.0, 2MR2.2

Problem-Solving Strategy: Use Logical Reasoning

Use logical reasoning to solve. **Show your work here.**

1. Anton, Lupe, and Sam measure their feet. They write down these lengths: 4 inches, 5 inches, and 7 inches. Sam's foot is longer than Lupe's foot. Anton's foot is not the shortest foot. Who has the shortest foot?

   ____

2. Ms. Kim trains dolphins to jump these heights: 5 feet, 2 yards, or 3 yards. Moe jumps higher than Skipper. Lulu jumps 1 foot shorter than Skipper. Which dolphin jumps 3 yards?

   ____

3. Chris sews a blanket, a flag, and a hat. He uses cloth in these lengths: 1 yard, 2 yards, and 3 yards. The flag uses more cloth than the hat. The blanket uses 3 yards of cloth. How much cloth is needed for the hat?

   ____________ yard(s)

Name ______________________________

12-5

Homework Practice

2MG1.3, 2MR2.2

Measure to the Nearest Centimeter

Chapter Resources

Preparation: A centimeter ruler is needed for this activity.

Use a centimeter ruler to measure.

1.

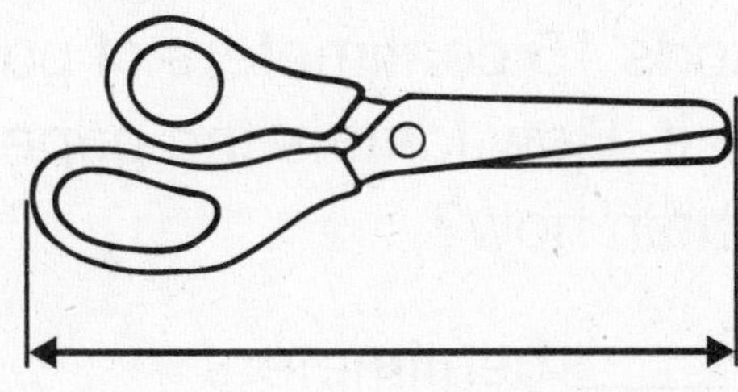

about ______ centimeters

2.

about ______ centimeters

3.

about ______ centimeters

4.

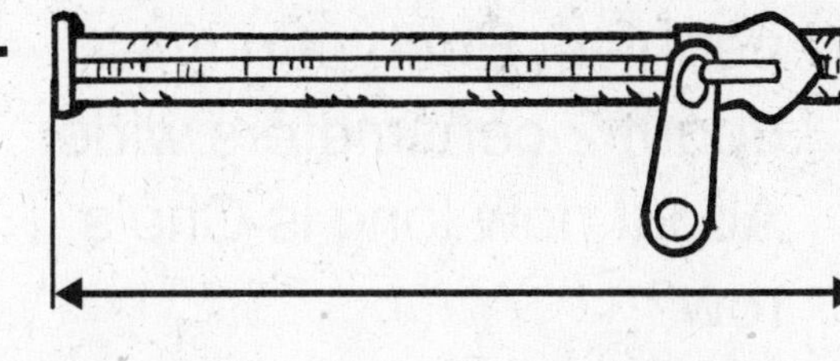

about ______ centimeters

5.

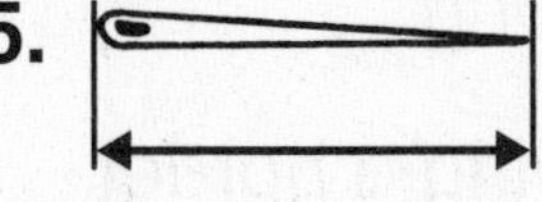

about ______ centimeters

6.

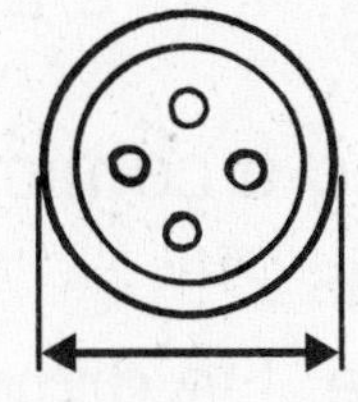

about ______ centimeters

Solve.

7. Ally slices carrots for dinner. Her carrot is 20 centimeters long. She needs carrot slices that are 3 centimeters long. Can she get 7 slices from her carrot?

____

8. Which is greater, the length of the button or the length of the needle? ____________

Name ______________________________

12-5

Problem-Solving Practice

2MG1.3, 2MR2.2

Measure to the Nearest Centimeter

Solve.

1. Kira is making a clay snake. Yesterday, it was 23 centimeters long. Today, it is 49 centimeters long. How many centimeters did Kira add?

   ______ centimeters

2. Stan has a paper chain that is 60 centimeters long. He adds 15 centimeters of paper to it. How long is the paper chain now?

   ______ centimeters

3. Cho makes a row of 23 pennies. Each penny is about 2 centimeters wide. About how long is Cho's row?

   The row is about ______ centimeters long.

4. Ty makes a paper clip chain that is 50 centimeters long. There are 10 paper clips in the chain. About how long is each paper clip?

   Each clip is about ______ centimeters long.

5. Ramon is making a comic strip. His paper is 24 centimeters wide. He draws panels that are 8 cenimeters wide. How many panels does Ramon have?

   ______ panels

6. Elena is drawing a border around a square picture. Each side of the picture is 10 centimeters long. How many total centimeters will the border be?

   ______ centimeters

Name ____________________

12-6

Homework Practice

2NS6.1, 2MG1.1

Centimeter and Meter

Preparation: A centimeter ruler and meter stick are needed for this activity.

Find the object. Use centimeters or meters. Estimate. Measure each item in the unit shown.

Find the Item	Estimate	Measure
1. foot	______ centimeters	______ centimeters
2. hand	______ centimeters	______ centimeters
3. parent	______ meters	______ meters

Solve.

4. Kal needs two 50-centimeter pieces of cloth. Can he cut what he needs from a one-meter length of cloth? ______

5. Mrs. Chen's desk is 120 centimeters from the window. Is the distance greater than or less than a meter? Write the difference.

   The distance is ______ centimeters ______________ than a meter.

6. Name three things in your home that are longer than a meter.

   ____

7. Name three things in your home that are shorter than a meter.

   ____

Name ___

12-6

Problem-Solving Practice

2NS6.1, 2MG1.1

Centimeter and Meter

Solve.

1. Rick's toy train is 1 meter long. Ali's toy train is 98 centimeters long. Who has the longer toy?

   ___

2. Lin's fish poster is 125 centimeters tall. Her cow poster is 1 meter and 25 centimeters tall. Which poster is shorter?

   ___

3. Jose is wrapping 8 gifts. He needs 50 centimeters of paper to wrap each one. How many meters of paper will he use?

   ___ meters

4. Mr. Kim is stacking 7 boxes. Each box is 30 centimeters tall. About how many meters tall is the stack of 7 boxes?

   about ___ meters

5. A stack of 5 nickels is about 1 centimeter tall. Cass puts her nickels in a stack. Her stack is about 16 centimeters tall. How many nickels does Cass have?

   She has ___ nickels.

6. Andre measures one penny. It is 2 centimeters wide. Next, Andre puts all his pennies in a row. The row is 64 centimeters long. How many pennies does Andre have?

   Andre has ___ pennies.

Name ______________________________

12-7

Homework Practice

2MG1.4, 2MR1.2

Time to the Quarter Hour

Chapter Resources

Use your clock. Draw the minute hand to show the time.

1. 3:45

3:15

3:30

2. 9:30

9:15

9:45

Solve.

3. Andy's music lesson is at a quarter after 4. It takes about 15 minutes to get to the lesson. At what time should Andy leave so he can get to his lesson on time?

____ : ____

4. Jen is going to a party that begins at 1:00. It will take Jen's mom 15 minutes to drive there. At what time should they leave for the party?

____ : ____

12-7

Name ______________________________

Problem-Solving Practice

2MG1.4

Time to the Quarter Hour

Solve.

1. The kickball team warms up for 15 minutes before each game. Today's game starts at 11:30.What time does warm up start?

   ____

2. Mia needs 30 minutes to get ready for her dance show. The show starts at 1:00. When should Mia begin to get ready?

   ____

3. Jin is visiting the dentist at 3:30. It takes his mom 15 minutes to drive there. At what time must Jin and his mom leave to get to his visit on time?

   ____

4. The bus driver leaves school at 3:15. She makes 3 stops. There are 15 minutes between each stop. When is the bus driver's last stop?

   ____

5. Dr. Cruz opens her office at 8:30. 3 people are in the waiting room. Dr. Cruz spends 15 minutes with each person. When does the last person leave?

   ____

6. At 3:00 Cal and Amy start baking cookies. Each pan of cookies bakes for a quarter hour. How many pans of cookies can they bake between 3:15 and 4:30?

   ____

Name ____________________

12-8

Homework Practice

2MR2.0, 2AF1.0

Problem-Solving Investigation: Choose a Strategy

Chapter Resources

Solve. Show your work.

1. The zookeeper feeds the baby tiger every 4 hours. The baby tiger eats at 8:30, 12:30, and at 4:30. When will the baby tiger eat next? ______

2. Evan's picture is 55 centimeters long and 45 centimeters wide. He wants to make a yarn border. How many meters of yarn does Evan need? (Hint: Remember there are 4 sides to a picture.)

   ______ meters

3. 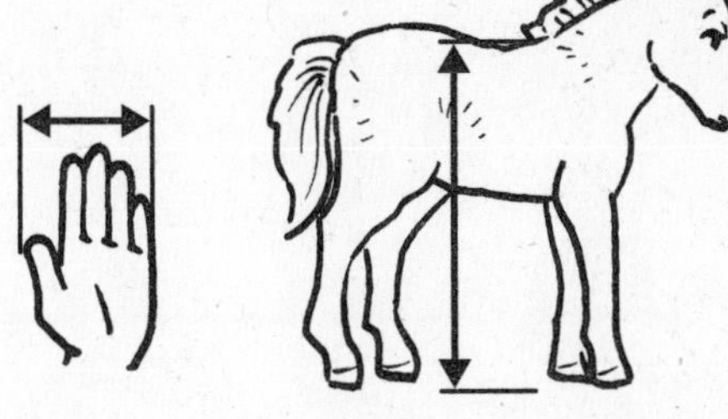

   Farmer Ben's pony is 9 hands tall. 1 hand is 4 inches. About how tall is the pony in feet?

   about ______ feet

Name ______________________________

12-9

Homework Practice

2MG1.5, 2MR1.2

Elapsed Time

Write each start time and each end time. Then write how much time as passed.

Activity	Start Time	End Time	How long does it take?
1. Go to Dentist	___ : ___	___ : ___	______ hour
2. Homework	___ : ___	___ : ___	______ hour
3. Baseball game	___ : ___	___ : ___	______ hours

Solve. Draw the clock hands to show the time.

4. Lu starts to build a model at 1:00. He spends 1 hour and 15 minutes building it. At what time is Lu's model done?

______

5. Ramon's family starts driving at 7:00. They arrive at Grandma's house four hours and 15 minutes later. At what time do they arrive?

______

Name ______________________________

12-9

Problem-Solving Practice

2MG1.5, 2MR1.2

Elapsed Time

Solve. Tell how much time has passed.

1. The dance lesson started at 10:00 A.M. It ended at 11:00 A.M. How long did the lesson last? ________ hour

2. The game started at 2:00 P.M. It ended at 4:00 P.M. How much time passed?

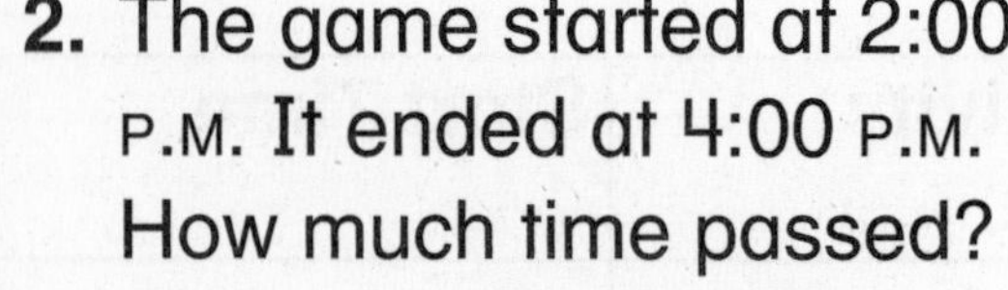

________ hours passed

3. Mei and Troy built a fort. They started at 1:00 P.M. They finished at 4:00 P.M. How many hours passed?

________ hours passed

4. Joey went for a horse ride. He left at 8:00 A.M. and got back at noon. How long did the horse ride last?

________ hours

5. Draw the hands on the clock to show each time.

Rosa is going on a trip to the lake. The bus leaves at 9:00 A.M. It gets to the lake at 1:00 P.M. How long will it take to get to the lake?

________ hours

6. Joni left Sara's house at 1:00 P.M. and went to Lucy's house. She left Lucy's house at 2:00 P.M. and went to Trish's house. Joni got home at 4:00 P.M. How many hours passed since Joni left Sara's house?

________ hours passed.

Name ___

12-10

Homework Practice

2MG1.4

Time Relationships

1 minute = 60 seconds	1 week = 7 days
1 hour = 60 minutes	1 month = 4 weeks
1 day = 24 hours	1 year = 12 months or 52 weeks

Circle the best unit to measure the time for each event.

1. to go to school

10 minutes 10 hours

2. to eat lunch

30 seconds 30 minutes

3. to sleep at night

8 minutes 8 hours

4. to bicycle to a friend's

30 minutes 30 days

Solve.

5. Nina goes to visit her aunt on Saturday at 9:15 in the morning. Her dad picks her up on Sunday morning at 11:15. How long is Nina at her aunt's house?

______ hours

Name ______________________________

12-10

Problem-Solving Practice

2MG1.4

Time Relationships

Solve. Use these time relationships.

1 minute = 60 seconds	1 week = 7 days
1 hour = 60 minutes	1 month = 4 weeks
1 day = 24 hours	1 year = 12 months or 52 weeks

1. Jerry's family camps for three days. They hike for 3 hours each day. By the end of trip, how many hours have they hiked? Write a number sentence to explain your answer.

   ______ ◯ ______ ◯ ______

   ______ hours

2. Rain starts at 9:00, Monday morning. It rains until 9:00, Wednesday morning. How long does it rain? Write a number sentence to explain your answer.

   ______ ◯ ______ ◯ ______

   ______ days or hours

3. Mark draws for 25 minutes. Then he eats lunch for 30 minutes. After lunch, Mark draws for 65 minutes. How long does Mark draw? Write two number sentences to explain your answer.

   65 + ______ = ______

   ______ − 60 = ______

   ______ hour ______ minutes or ______ minutes

13-1

Name ____________________

Homework Practice

2NS2.2, 2AF1.0

Add Hundreds

Chapter Resources

Add.

1. 300 + 100 = ____   200 + 400 = ____   700 + 100 = ____   200 + 300 = ____   100 + 400 = ____

2. 600 + 100 = ____   300 + 200 = ____   600 + 200 = ____   800 + 100 = ____   400 + 500 = ____

3. 500 + 200 = ____   400 + 200 = ____   500 + 300 = ____   200 + 200 = ____   100 + 700 = ____

4. 300 + 300 = ____   400 + 300 = ____   100 + 100 = ____   200 + 200 = ____   100 + 800 = ____

Solve.

5. There are 400 students in the second grade. There are 400 students in the third grade. How many students are there in all?

_____ students

6. 400 parents came to the school concert on Thursday. 500 parents came to the school concert on Friday. How many total parents came to the concerts?

_____ parents

7. Look back over this page. Circle every answer that is greater than 450.

Name ______________________

13-1

Problem-Solving Practice

2NS2.2, 2AF1.0

Add Hundreds

Solve.

1. The fair comes to town. There are 300 yellow balloons and 200 green balloons. How many balloons are there in all?

3 hundreds + 2 hundreds =

____ hundreds

2. There are 500 blue streamers and 200 orange streamers. How many streamers are there in all?

5 hundreds + 2 hundreds =

____ hundreds

500 + 200 = ____

3. 200 girls and 200 boys go to the fair on Saturday. How many go on Saturday in all?

200 + 200 = ____ children

4. The fair sells 400 tickets on Saturday and 500 on Sunday. How many tickets are sold in all?

400 + 500 = ____ tickets

Fair Snack-Stand Sales

Snack	Saturday	Sunday
Bags of popcorn	400	200
Bags of peanuts	300	400

5. How many bags of popcorn were sold in all?

____

How many bags of peanuts were sold in all?

____

6. Were more bags of popcorn sold or peanuts sold?

____

____

Name ________________

13-2

Homework Practice

2NS2.2, 2AF1.2

Regroup Ones

Chapter Resources

Preparation: Base-ten blocks are needed for this activity.

Use [ten-rod] **to add.**

1.

	hundreds	tens	ones
		1	
	4	6	9
+	2	2	5
	6	9	4

2.

	hundreds	tens	ones
		☐	
	2	5	4
+	3	2	8

3.

	hundreds	tens	ones
		☐	
	2	5	8
+	7	2	9

4.

	hundreds	tens	ones
	5	3	2
+	2	5	5

5. 352 + 439 = ______

6. 283 + 709 = ______

7. 605 + 176 = ______

8. 819 + 104 = ______

9. 411 + 269 = ______

10. 737 + 146 = ______

Solve.

11. Ms. Kim's class has 486 blocks. Mr. Vega's class has 406 blocks. How many total blocks?______

12. Find the pattern. Fill in the missing numbers.

911, 902, 893, ______, ______, 866, ______

Name ____________________

13-2

Problem-Solving Practice

2NS2.2, 2AF1.2

Regroup Ones

Preparation: Extra paper is needed for this activity.

Solve. Use another sheet of paper to regroup the ones, if needed.

1. There are 127 blue flags and 133 white flags. How many flags are there all together?

   ______ flags

2. The circus travels 246 miles on Tuesday. It travels 225 miles on Wednesday. How many miles does it travel in all?

   ______ miles

3. The circus performed 247 days last year. It performed 235 days the year before. How many days did it perform in those two years?

   ______ days

4. There are two tigers in the circus. One tiger weighs 206 pounds. The other tiger weighs 188 pounds. How much do they weigh together?

   ______ pounds

5. The circus orders 348 pounds of hay from Farmer Green and 437 pounds of hay from Farmer Brown. How many pounds does the circus order in all?

   ______ pounds

6. The circus spends 466 dollars on food and 329 dollars on water. How much money does it spend on food and water?

   ______ dollars

   Does it spend **more** or **less** than $800? ______

Name ____________________

13-3

Homework Practice

2NS2.2, 2MR1.2

Regroup Tens

Chapter Resources

Preparation: Base-ten blocks are needed for this activity.

Use [tens block] to add.

1.

	hundreds	tens	ones
	□		
	3	4	2
+	3	6	7

2.

	hundreds	tens	ones
	□		
	4	8	4
+	1	5	3

3. 653 + 251 = ______

4. 598 + 260 = ______

5. 168 + 740 = ______

6. 472 + 242 = ______

7. 284 + 190 = ______

8. 374 + 375 = ______

Solve. Use [tens block], if needed.

9. Kip's grade has 247 students. His sister Myra's grade has 368 students. How many students in all?

______ students

10. Write the answers to problems 1–2 in expanded form.

______ + ______ + ______ = ______

______ + ______ + ______ = ______

Name ______________________

13-3

Problem-Solving Practice

2NS2.2, 2MR1.2

Regroup Tens

Preparation: Base-ten blocks are needed for this activity.

Solve. Use [tens block], if needed.

1. Jim has 358 rubber bands. He finds 251 more. How many rubber bands in all?

	hundreds	tens	ones
	☐		
	3	5	8
+	2	5	1

2. Ling has 426 pennies. Pam has 392 pennies. How many pennies in all?

	hundreds	tens	ones
	☐		
	4	2	6
+	3	9	2

3. Marie buys a hot dog for 165 cents and a soda for 150 cents.

   How many cents does she spend in all? ______ cents

4. Freda buys a hamburger for 270 cents and a milk shake for 155 cents.

   How many cents does she spend in all? ______ cents

5. Jake and Trey save money for the zoo. Jake has 462 pennies. Trey has 386 pennies. How many pennies in all? ______ pennies

6. Tickets are 4 dollars each. Do Jake and Trey have enough money for the zoo?

   ______

13-4

Name ______________________________

Homework Practice

2AF1.3, 2MR1.0

Problem-Solving Strategy: Make a Table

Chapter Resources

Use the table to solve.

1. Randall keeps track of how many lawns he mows each week. If the pattern goes on, how many lawns will he mow in week 4?

Week	Number of Lawns
1	7
2	10
3	13
4	______

2. Mr. Ray's class is going to the history museum. He made a list of the activities for the day.

Museum Trip	
See film: World Art	11:15–12:15
Lunch	12:30–1:00
History of Egypt	1:15–2:15

For how long will they see the Egypt display? ______________

3. A restaurant serves 40 oranges a day. How many oranges does it serve in 5 days?

days					
oranges					

Name ______________________________

13-5

Homework Practice

2NS2.0, 2NS6.0

Estimate Sums

Chapter Resources

Round each number to the nearest *ten*.
Estimate the sum.

1. 149 →
+ 366 → +

2. 514 →
+ 233 → +

3. 295 →
+ 480 → +

4. 170 →
+ 396 → +

Round each number to the nearest *hundred*.
Estimate the sum.

5. 811 →
+ 117 → +

6. 502 →
+ 710 → +

7. 199 →
+ 540 → +

8. 287 →
+ 132 → +

Solve.

9. Jack's school has a book sale. They sell 347 books on Monday and 214 books on Tuesday. Rounding to the nearest ten, how many books does the school sell?

_______ books

Name ______________________________

13-5

Problem-Solving Practice

2NS2.0, 2NS6.0

Estimate Sums

Solve.

1. Mr. Marcus sells 313 oranges and 196 apples. Round to the nearest ten and estimate how many fruits Mr. Marcus sells.

   _______ fruits

2. There are 217 adults and 489 children at the zoo. Round to the nearest hundred and estimate how many people are at the zoo.

   _______ people

3. Manuel has 390 pennies. His brother Carlos has 179 pennies. Round to the nearest hundred and estimate how many pennies the brothers have.

   _______ pennies

4. The Community Center has a bake sale. They sell 219 churros on Saturday and 189 churros on Sunday. Round to the nearest ten and estimate how many churros the Community Center sells.

   _______ churros

5. Tanner's class read 110 books last year. They read 129 books this year. Estimate how many books the class read in the two years. Round to the nearest hundred.

   _______ books

6. The second grade at Campbell Elementary School has 311 students. The third grade has 391 students. Estimate how many students there are in the two grades. Round to the nearest ten.

   _______ students

Name ____________________

13-6

Homework Practice

2NS2.2, 2NS5.0

Add Money

Chapter Resources

Solve.

1. $6.06 + 1.23

2. $3.55 + 2.89

3. $0.77 + 2.19

4. $8.23 + 1.59

5. $5.05 + 2.46

6. $1.39 + 4.50

Use the table to solve.

Lunch #1	$3.49	add juice	$0.75
Lunch #2	$3.79	add milk	$0.75
Lunch #3	$4.10	add orange	$0.89
Lunch #4	$4.75	add yogurt	$1.23

7. Brady wants to buy lunch #2. He would also like to add an orange. How much will Brady's lunch cost?

____

8. Mrs. Stone buys lunch #4. She adds both a yogurt and a juice. What is the total cost of her lunch?

____

Name ______________________

13-6

Problem-Solving Practice

2NS2.2, 2NS5.0

Add Money

Solve.

1. Kate buys a pen for $2.00. She buys a notebook for $1.69. How much does Kate spend in all?

____

2. Dan saves $4.75. He puts another $1.26 in his bank. How much money does Dan have now?

____

3. Drew wants to buy the boat for his sister and the train for his brother. How much will he spend in all?

____

4. Mrs. Magee sells a boat and a bear. How much money does she earn?

____

Special #1	$6.59	Add coffee	$1.10
Special #2	$7.59	Add rolls	$0.84
Special #3	$7.95	Add soup	$1.73

5. Mr. Grey orders special #2 and adds rolls. How much is Mr. Grey's dinner?

____

6. Mrs. Grey orders special #1 and adds soup. How much is Mrs. Grey's dinner?

____

Name ________________________________

13-7

Homework Practice

2MR1.1, 2NS2.2

Problem-Solving Investigation: Choose a Strategy

Problem-Solving Strategies

- Use Logical Reasoning
- Make a Chart
- Write a Number Sentence

1. Ken buys the duck and the fish. He thinks the total will be less than $4.00. Is he correct? Explain.

____

2. Raj buys the boat to share with his brother. If he also buys the frog, how much will he spend altogether?

____

3. Name the two most expensive items shown above. What would be the total cost of these two items?

____

4. Billy has $5.00 to spend. What 3 items can Billy buy?

____

Name ______________________________

14-1

Homework Practice

2NS2.2, 2MR3.0

Subtract Hundreds

Chapter Resources

Solve.

1. 400 − 200 = ____ 700 − 200 = ____ 900 − 400 = ____ 800 − 400 = ____

2. 600 − 300 = ____ 800 − 700 = ____ 500 − 100 = ____ 400 − 100 = ____

3. 900 − 700 = ____ 700 − 200 = ____ 800 − 200 = ____ 900 − 200 = ____

4. 600 − 200 = ____ 900 − 100 = ____ 300 − 200 = ____ 500 − 200 = ____

Solve.

Show your work here.

5. Tam's class sells 500 raffle tickets. Leah's class sells 400 raffle tickets. How many more tickets does Tam's class sell?

______ more tickets

Name ______________________________

14-1

Problem-Solving Practice

2NS2.2, 2AF1.0

Subtract Hundreds

Solve.

1. There are 300 balls. Take away 100 balls. How many balls are left?

3 hundreds – 1 hundred =

______ hundreds

300 – 100 = ______ balls

2. There are 400 paper clips. Take away 200 paper clips. How many are left?

4 hundreds – 2 hundreds =

______ hundreds

400 – 200 = ______ balls

3. Allison has 500 marbles. She gives Jimmy 300. How many marbles does Allison have left?

______ – ______ = ______

marbles

4. Paul has 600 baseball cards. He gives his brother 200. How many cards does Paul have left?

______ – ______ = ______

cards

5. Jim and Tad have 400 stickers. 200 of those stickers belong to Jim. How many belong to Tad?

______ – ______ = ______

Which boy has more stickers?

____

____

6. Abby has 900 pennies. She traded 500 pennies. How many pennies does she have left?

______ – ______ = ______

How many dollar bills did she get for 500 pennies?

______ bills

Name ______________________________

14-2

Homework Practice

2NS2.2, 2MR1.2

Regroup Tens

Chapter Resources

Solve.

1.

hundreds	tens	ones
6 – 2	5 1	2 4

2.

hundreds	tens	ones
7 – 5	7 5	3 9

3.

hundreds	tens	ones
4 – 3	6 1	6 9

4.

hundreds	tens	ones
3 – 2	4 2	4 7

5. 766 – 136 = ______

6. 886 – 53 = ______

7. 694 – 347 = ______

8. 964 – 467 = ______

Solve.

9. 536 people see the volcano on Saturday. 319 people visit on Sunday. How many more people saw the volcano on Saturday?

______ people

10. Workers make 248 dolls on Monday. The next day, they make 129 dolls. How many more dolls do they make on Monday?

______ dolls

Name ______________________________

14-2

Problem-Solving Practice

2NS2.2, 2MR1.2

Regroup Tens

Write the answer. Show your work.

1. Mr. Fino has a fruit stand. He has 245 apples. He sells 127 apples. How many apples are left?

______ apples

hundreds	tens	ones
	☐	☐
2 − 1	4 2	5 7

2. There are 364 oranges. 155 oranges are sold. How many oranges are left?

______ oranges

hundreds	tens	ones
	☐	☐
3 − 1	6 5	4 5

3. Ms. Florio's bakery has 254 cookies. She sells 127. How many cookies are left?

______ cookies

4. There are 367 cakes. She sells 139 cakes. How many cakes are left?

______ cakes

5. There are 465 roses on Monday. On Tuesday, 132 roses are sold. On Wednesday, 114 roses are sold. How many roses are left on Wednesday?

______ roses left

Show how you can subtract two times to find the answer.

____

____

Name ______

14-3

Homework Practice

2NS2.2, 2AF1.0

Regroup Hundreds

Chapter Resources

Use models and WorkMat 7. Subtract.

1. 336 – 254 = ______

2. 755 – 574 = ______

3. 748 – 280 = ______

4. 976 – 886 = ______

5. 559 – 122 = ______

6. 614 – 441 = ______

7. 750 – 230 = ______

8. 439 – 272 = ______

9. 131 – 85 = ______

10. 381 – 191 = ______

11. 893 – 329 = ______

12. 940 – 542 = ______

Solve.

13. Kyle takes 319 melons to market. He sells 245 melons. How many melons does Kyle have left?

______ melons

14. Ms. Jensen's bakery gives 228 cookies to the fund-raiser. 186 of the cookies are sold. How many cookies are leftover?

______ cookies

14-3

Name ______________________________

Problem-Solving Practice

2NS2.2, 2AF1.0

Regroup Hundreds

Solve.

1. There are 339 paper cups. The class uses 152. How many cups are left?

_______ cups

hundreds	tens	ones
□ 3 – 1	□ 3 5	 9 2

2. There are 455 paper plates. The class uses 263. How many plates are left?

_______ plates

hundreds	tens	ones
□ 4 – 2	□ 5 6	 5 3

3. Mrs. Garza's trip is 457 miles long. She has already gone 274 miles. How many miles are left to go?

_______ miles

4. There are 368 children at the fair. 185 of them are boys. How many are girls?

_______ girls

5. The Travel Club has 846 dollars. They go on a trip to the beach. A bus costs 450 dollars to rent. How much money does the club have left over?

_______ dollars

6. The Travel Club pays for snacks and drinks. Snacks cost 146 dollars. Drinks cost 163 dollars. How much money is left at the end of the trip?

_______ dollars

Name ____________________

14-4

Homework Practice

2MR2.2, 2AF1.0

Problem-Solving Strategy: Guess and Check

Solve. Circle the correct answers.

1. Mary and Margeret are in a Walk-A-Thon to raise money for charity. The 2 women walked a total of 43 miles. How many miles might each woman have walked?

   20, 25, 17, 18, 27

2. What number am I?
   I am more than 600.
   I have a 8 in the ones place.
   The sum of my three numbers is 18

   728, 558, 639, 828, 657

3. Kedrick has 44 rubber balls. In honor of his favorite team, the balls are either orange or blue. How many and what color might each of them be?

   orange 29, orange 15, blue 27, blue 15

4. Ron, Vic, and Tan each collect recyclable cans. Over a weekend, the 3 collected 101 cans in all. How many might each of them have collected?

   40, 39, 35, 29, 22

14-5

Name ______________________________

Homework Practice

2NS2.0, 2NS6.0

Estimate Differences

From:	To:	Distance:
Seattle, WA	Boise, ID	397 miles
Seattle, WA	Portland, OR	129 miles

1. Rounding to the nearest hundred, estimate how many more miles it is from Seattle to Boise than from Seattle to Portland?

   Show your work. ______ miles

From:	To:	Distance:
Dallas, TX	New Orleans, LA	448 miles
Dallas, TX	Phoenix, AZ	865 miles

2. Rounding to the nearest ten, estimate how many more miles it is from Dallas to Phoenix than from Dallas to New Orleans?

   Show your work. ______ miles

Round to the nearest *ten* to estimate.

3. $425 - 374$ $\quad$ $556 - 225$ $\quad$ $847 - 161$ $\quad$ $770 - 166$

Round to the nearest *hundred* to estimate.

4. $402 - 181$ $\quad$ $911 - 337$ $\quad$ $605 - 380$ $\quad$ $992 - 79$

Name ____________________

14-5

Problem-Solving Practice

2NS2.0, 2NS6.0

Estimate Differences

From:	To:	Distance:
Tulsa, OK	Denver, CO	540 miles
Baltimore, MD	Trenton, NJ	125 miles

1. Rounding to the nearest hundred, how many more miles is it from Tulsa to Denver than from Baltimore to Trenton? Show your work. ______ miles

From:	To:	Distance:
Indianapolis, IN	Memphis, TN	382 miles
Atlanta, GA	Raleigh, NC	356 miles

2. Rounding to the nearest ten, how many more miles is it from Indianapolis to Memphis than from Atlanta to Raleigh? Show your work. ______ miles

Solve.

3. There are 861 people in Apple Ridge. There are 647 people in Blue Bay. Rounding to the nearest ten, estimate how many more people live in Apple Ridge. ______________

4. 304 people went skiing on Mt. White last weekend. This weekend, 491 people ski there. Round to the nearest hundred and estimate how many more people skied this weekend. ______________

Name ____________________

14-6

Homework Practice

2NS2.2, 2NS5.0

Subtract Money

Chapter Resources

Subtract. Show your work.

1. $6.11 − 4.26	**2.** $9.31 − 7.87	**3.** $4.21 − 2.22	**4.** $8.01 − 3.50
5. $3.25 − 2.95	**6.** $2.79 − 1.29	**7.** $7.62 − 4.03	**8.** $5.55 − 2.78
9. $5.51 − 3.60	**10.** $6.64 − 1.58	**11.** $8.65 − 4.53	**12.** $9.73 − 5.70

Solve.

13. Mick has $3.30. His bus ride will cost him $2.50. How much money will he have left? ______

14. Deena has $4.25 for lunch. A sandwich and chips costs $3.50 and an apple is 50 cents. Will Deena have any money left over? How much? ____________________

15. Wade has $3.65. He wants to buy a comic book for $2.75. How much money will he have left? ______

16. Carmen has $6.29 for a snack and movie ticket. The ticket costs $4.95. How much money is left for a snack? ______

Name ________________________________

14-6 Problem-Solving Practice

2NS2.2, 2NS5.0

Subtract Money

Write the answer.

1. Kate has $3.27. She buys a magazine that costs $2.85. How much does she have left?

_______ – _______ = _______

2. Harry has $7.38. He buys a pen for $3.76. How much does he have left?

_______ – _______ = _______

3. Zoe has $8.25. She wants to buy a scarf for $5.85. How much money will she have left?

$8.25
– $5.85

4. Dee has $9.00 for a hat and scarf. The hat costs $4.76. The scarf costs $3.42. If she buys both, how much money will Dee have left?

$4.76
+3.42

$9.00
– _______

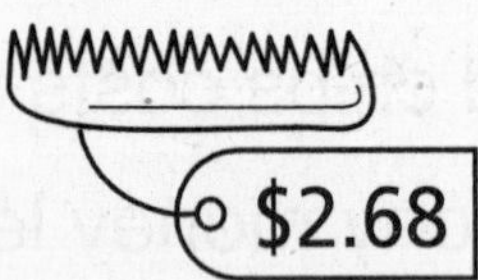

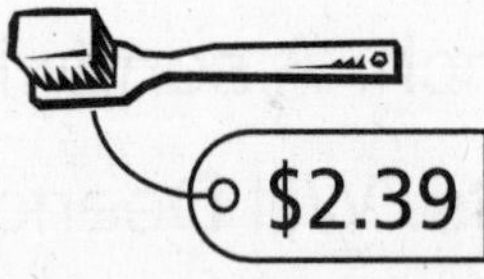

5. Norm has $5.00. How much will he have left if he buys the comb?

____

6. How much will Norm have left if he buys both the toothbrush and toothpaste?

____

Name ____________________

14-7

Homework Practice

2NS2.2, 2MR1.1

Problem-Solving Investigation: Choose a Strategy

Chapter Resources

Write the answer.

1. The book is 246 pages long. Tess has already read 128 pages. How many pages are left to read?

```
  246
- 128
```

______ pages left

2. Mr. Finn has 181 nails. He uses 132. How many nails are left?

```
  181
- 132
```

______ nails

3. It is 748 miles from Davis to Blue Gorge. Ms. Peck has already driven 365 miles. How many more miles does she still have to drive?

______ more miles

4. Al buys a birthday card for $1.75. He had $2.50. How much money does he have now?

____

5. Maple School is putting on a talent show. 1st grade sells 50 tickets. 2nd grade sells 100 tickets. 3rd grade sells 150 tickets. If the pattern continues, how many tickets will 4th grade sell?

______ tickets

6. Anthony has $9.00. He wants to buy some presents. A game costs $3.75. A kite costs $5.34. A poster costs $4.25. Which two presents can he buy?

____